Successful Professional
for Civil Engineers

Fourth edition

ice
Institution of Civil Engineers

publishing

Successful Professional Reviews for Civil Engineers

Fourth edition

Patrick Waterhouse
H. Macdonald Steels

Published by ICE Publishing, One Great George Street, Westminster, London SW1P 3AA.

Full details of ICE Publishing sales representatives and distributors can be found at:
www.icebookshop.com/bookshop_contact.asp

First edition published 1997
Second edition published 2006
Third edition published 2011. Reprinted 2013, 2014
Fourth edition published 2015. Reprinted 2017, 2018, 2019, 2020

Other titles by ICE Publishing:
Dynamic Mentoring for Civil Engineers.
H. M. Steels. ISBN 0-7277-3003-7
Initial Professional Development for Civil Engineers.
H. M. Steels. ISBN 0-7277-4147-9
Civil Engineering Procedure.
M. Kennard. ISBN 978-0-7277-3524-9

www.icevirtuallibrary.com

A catalogue record for this book is available from the British Library

ISBN 978-0-7277-6100-2

© Thomas Telford Limited 2015

ICE Publishing is a division of Thomas Telford Ltd, a wholly-owned subsidiary of the Institution of Civil Engineers (ICE).

Commissioning Editor: Gavin Jamieson
Production Editor: Rebecca Taylor
Market Development Executive: Elizabeth Hobson

Typeset by Academic + Technical, Bristol
Index created by Indexing Specialists (UK) Ltd, Hove, East Sussex
Printed and bound in Great Britain by Bell and Bain, Glasgow

Contents

Preface

Early in 2015, the Institution of Civil Engineers (ICE) simplified the process of applying for membership and made it applicable to most potential Members, irrespective of their starting point. Initial Professional Development is now based on a framework of the same Attributes as are needed to demonstrate competence at the Professional Review.

The other significant changes include the move to electronic submissions and the withdrawal of the ICE Guidance Notes. There is therefore an ongoing need for the advice and guidance contained in this book.

The joint authors have co-operated on delivering seminars and tutorials on professional development for several years, utilising a wealth of knowledge and experience from two different professional backgrounds. Having retired recently, 'Mac' has collaborated with his erstwhile colleague Patrick to update this book to its fourth edition.

We are grateful for the enthusiastic encouragement and active co-operation of many staff of the Institution, particularly in the North West England Region, as well as a continuing dialogue with several current Reviewers, Delegated and Supervising Engineers and trainees.

Yet again, we are indebted to so many people:

- the Reviewers, who share their experience and thoughts
- the Institution's Membership staff, who explained the changes to us, particularly Gillian Elvy
- our contacts throughout the profession, who have assisted with our development of this book
- our respective families, who continue to humour, encourage and support us, almost without complaint.

Patrick Waterhouse and H. Macdonald Steels, July 2015

Successful Professional Reviews for Civil Engineers
ISBN 978-0-7277-6100-2

ICE Publishing: All rights reserved
http://dx.doi.org/10.1680/sprce61002.001

Chapter 1
The role of the profession

On behalf of its members and in its capacity of acting in the public interest, the Institution of Civil Engineers continues to take a leading role in the debates on the environment, green energy, climate change and what has become known as 'sustainability' – 'meet[ing] the needs of the present without compromising the ability of future generations to meet their own needs' (World Commission on Environment and Development, 1987, p. 43). Note the use of the word 'needs', not 'wants' or 'desires'. In highly developed parts of the world, it is easy for people to forget what we actually need, as distinct from what we believe we deserve.

With this increasing emphasis on sustainable development, the civil engineer, with the ability to take the broad view and positively seek acceptable compromise, is well placed to make the distinction between the needs and the wants or desires of an increasingly affluent society – a developed world which has progressed far beyond the basic necessities of clean water, food and shelter and which rising economies, understandably, now seek to emulate. Can we, for example, help these emerging economies to avoid some of the serious mistakes that developed countries have made?

Much of our society has vested interests – what former ICE President David Green described as 'single issue politics' – manifested in the uncompromising pressure group. Civil engineers can rise above these vested interests, to 'utilise scarce resources, care for the environment and protect the safety and health of the public' (ICE Royal Charter 1972). We have moved away from former perceptions – no longer 'predict and provide' but 'target and manage', and must persuade the public of the validity and good sense of our pragmatism.

So, the emphasis of the profession continues to move further towards the maintenance and the efficient and better usage of existing assets; towards revolutionary and sustainable solutions to ever-greater environmental, social and geographical problems, well beyond what has been considered traditional ('design and build') civil engineering.

The range of abilities which the public, society and clients need in professional engineers today is very different from those which were required only a couple of generations ago. There are engineers becoming professionally qualified through the Reviews who are implementing solutions which do not involve traditional construction at all. While many younger engineers continue to be involved with conventional design and construction, the profession is playing an increasing role in deciding what is appropriate and they must expect to become involved in this aspect.

ICE qualification system

The Institution of Civil Engineers' qualification system made the transition to provide for these growing needs when it first published the ICE 3000 *Routes to Membership* series over ten years ago. That series set out nine Attributes against which every candidate would be reviewed, of which only two were technical. In addition, the Review procedures meant that your Initial Professional Development (IPD) would be ratified either by your Supervising Civil Engineer (SCE) (if under Agreement) or by the Institution through a Career Appraisal and would not be part of the Review process. This was a significant shift from the 'process' to the 'product' of training, from 'What have you done?' to 'What have you become?' as a result of that experience. That shift is consolidated in the streamlined Review system introduced at the beginning of 2015.

Detailed changes to the Review system will, of course, continue to ensure that those becoming professionally qualified continue to meet the developing needs of our profession and the demanding societies we serve. But the fundamental philosophy behind the Reviews (as quoted above from our Royal Charter) remains constant and must be kept in mind throughout. The streamlining of the process of Review which prompted this new edition has neither diminished nor increased the standards that must be met to become professionally qualified.

The criteria for Membership (MICE) of the Institution are capable of wide interpret- ation, while still being applicable to the more traditional engineer. It is clear (but even now rumours persist) that there is no Institution requirement for specific experience in any particular work environment. Nowhere do the criteria refer to 'construction', 'reinforced concrete', 'site', 'design', 'calculations', 'bills of quantities' or 'rates build- up'. Confidence with analysis software does not, of itself, necessarily demonstrate an understanding of technical principles. Conversely, it is not necessary to do analysis in order to develop an understanding of technical principles. Many of you will use some (or many) of these specifics to develop the necessary qualities, but they are not absolute requirements.

We have personally guided civil engineers to success at the Professional Reviews with employers outside the generally accepted sphere of civil engineering companies: these include house builders, estate agents, telephone companies, commercial insurers, a merchant bank and even a firm of solicitors. These examples are, without doubt, extreme cases of highly specialised engineering, but they do emphasise the flexibility inherent in the Institution's criteria.

It is vital that trainees, their mentors and employers, recognise that old-fashioned stereo-types are no longer the mainstream. The flexibility which the Institution built into its training and Review systems with the advent of the 3000 series is at last starting to deliver the Institution's stated aim – a wider membership.

The Engineering Council

The Engineering Council (EC) is a quasi-autonomous non-governmental organisation (QUANGO) and regulates the basic qualifications of all UK professional engineers, whatever their discipline. It sets out benchmark standards for their academic education and requirements for their professional qualifications in three grades – Incorporated Engineer (IEng), Chartered Engineer (CEng) and Engineering Technician (EngTech).

The EC academic benchmarks are:

- for Incorporated Engineer (IEng), an accredited three-year full-time BEng or BSc degree in engineering
- for Chartered Engineers (CEng), an accredited four-year full-time MEng degree in engineering
- the benchmarks for Engineering Technician vary from National Vocational Qualifications (NVQs) to City and Guilds and others. We recommend that you seek advice as early as possible to establish the most appropriate course for you.

Within this EC framework, nominated engineering Institutions set their own standards of qualification, but also offer the EC designatory letters IEng, CEng or EngTech. ICE, as one of these nominated bodies, thus offers qualifying classes of Member (MICE, either at IEng or CEng) and Engineering Technician (EngTech TMICE), as well as others not recognised by the EC (see below).

Some senior engineers are still training graduates in much the same way as they were trained themselves, on the presumption that nothing has changed and that all their competent graduates will, inevitably, become Chartered Members. This is no longer the case. The historical mainstream member of our profession is now best matched by the EC description of the Incorporated Engineer, a highly competent technical manager.

The EC, despite continued resistance in certain areas of engineering, is unlikely to stray from its stated policy that the majority of professional engineers in the future will be IEng, in line with *all* the other countries in the European Union, where the Technical Engineer (our IEng) is generally held in very high regard. The corollary is surely that there will be fewer Chartered Engineers. However, progress since the introduction of the 3000 series has not led to a material change in the balance between Incorporated and Chartered Members.

Both are vital components of any engineering team, crudely divided into 'doers and managers of the doing' (IEng) and those who 'decide what needs to be done and persuade others of its appropriateness' (CEng), although there is inevitably a considerable overlap. This is why both Chartered Engineers and Incorporated Engineers have for some time been designated Corporate Members, MICE (IEng or CEng).

At the time when most graduates feel ready for Review, it is probable that they are somewhere between the two classes in terms of their professional development. It is likely that they will satisfy the requirements of the Member Professional Review for IEng MICE within a realistic timescale (say, three to four years). Some will develop the wider abilities embracing social, environmental and economic decision-making during that time or later and thus develop the attributes expected of a Chartered Member.

It is imperative that every candidate is clear on the requirements and chooses to apply for the class of membership in which they can most readily demonstrate the requisite attributes *at that time*. Their submission must be slanted towards either IEng or CEng, as appropriate. Each sponsoring firm or engineer must positively contribute to deciding which is the most appropriate designation for each individual approaching the Professional Review.

If you want to be a Chartered Engineer, then you must be much more aware of the wider aspects of our profession and of the involvement of your employer in the whole business of civil engineering. From an early stage in your development, you will be demonstrating clear signs of wide vision and strong leadership, wanting speedy and successful outcomes, seeking opportunities both for yourself and for your employer, aware of the whole range of influences on your work well beyond the technical. You must define and drive your own career aspirations, not wait for your employer to decide.

There is no disgrace whatsoever in graduates who feel comfortable doing so remaining within a technical role, but they cannot expect to become Chartered Engineers; they now have their own Engineering Council category.

There is still sometimes an unrealistic belief that, merely because you have satisfied the basic academic requirement, progression to Chartered status is somehow inevitable. Employers should discourage this belief in cases where it is clear that such progression is unlikely 'for the foreseeable future' (though no one should ever categorically rule out late development).

Wider membership

The Institution has developed agreements with Institutions worldwide:

- A number of Mutual Exemption Agreements exist with comparable organisations in many other countries. If you hold a professional qualification from outside the

UK, it is worth finding out from the Institution if such an Agreement exists with your qualifying body.

- If you are professionally qualified in another country of the European Union, then there is the European Directive Route which may allow your qualification to be recognised by the Institution.
- If you have been awarded IEng, CEng or EngTech through another nominated UK Institution, then you may become a member of the ICE.

In any of these scenarios, you should talk to the Institution as soon as possible to determine which is the most appropriate route for you. We continue to be amazed by the number of people who make unrealistic judgements about what they need to do, with the result that they waste a great deal of their own time and effort in abortive work.

Achieving membership

The emphasis of professional qualification has veered away from what a candidate has done, to whether the candidate satisfies all the defined Attributes ('product not process'). Consequently, the Institution is able to widen its membership without necessarily satisfying the Engineering Council's criteria for their academic qualifications (which means that certain members may not be able to use the designatory letters CEng or IEng).

Almost anyone who has the ability, aptitude and determination can become a member of the ICE, by successfully demonstrating that their experience has properly compensated for any perceived shortfall in their academic education. One of our most satisfying cases was a former bricklayer who needed to be professionally qualified to continue his career beyond site agent. His only academic qualification was a GCSE in mathematics, gained to help his children with their school work. He proudly satisfied the standards for CEng MICE after some years of determined effort.

For those who do have some academic qualifications, but which are not equivalent to the appropriate EC benchmark, the Institution offers a number of means by which qualifications already gained can be topped up to match the benchmarks, through further academic learning and/or work-based experience. We strongly advise you to submit yourself for an Assessment before embarking on any of these, so that ICE staff can give you current guidance and help.

The Institution also offers several means of qualifying for membership for those who do not match the EC's benchmark academic qualifications and are unable or unwilling to top up their academic qualifications. You are strongly advised to contact the ICE at an early stage to ascertain with certainty which of the alternatives best suits your personal circumstances.

For all of the available options, the guidance and advice given in this book is still useful, but must be tailored to suit the specific submission and interview being considered. The one route which has a specific report (the Technical Report) unlike any other route, is the Technical Report Route, for which there is advice and guidance in the final chapter of this book, Chapter 18.

Successful Professional Reviews for Civil Engineers
ISBN 978-0-7277-6100-2

ICE Publishing: All rights reserved
http://dx.doi.org/10.1680/sprce61002.007

Chapter 2
The jigsaw concept for Review preparation

When Mac was helping his young grandson build a jigsaw, he realised that they were doing exactly what every candidate for Review must do – construct a jigsaw. It was no good trying to find a piece with the correct shape; what they had to do was find a piece which added to the picture. Each piece had to be examined in detail to see how the part picture on it interlocked with the bits of picture on the pieces alongside. Continual reference had to be made to the picture on the box to see the position of each piece in the complete picture. It was no good picking up pieces which looked as though they might be the correct shape without looking at the picture on the box, just as it is no good picking a particular piece of experience because it appeals to you or because it seems to fit the space. The process mirrors precisely the system which we recommend for compilation of your Review.

All the components of the Review, the documents making up the submission, the interview and the Written Exercise, are each an essential part of the whole picture. They form the pieces of your jigsaw, but the size and shape of each piece will vary from candidate to candidate. All the pieces are important; none can be omitted. Everyone remembers how frustrating it is when one final piece of a jigsaw is missing or is a bit mangled; you must not leave any possibility that the Reviewers might feel that same frustration.

The picture is similar for everybody – either MICE or AMICE, as indicated here:

But the separate pieces are different shapes and sizes for each individual – no two jigsaws will ever have the same shape or size of pieces:

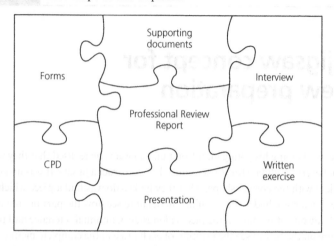

This is why it is no good copying someone else's submission: it probably will not work for you. It is also why the Institution is very reluctant to publish examples of successful work, either for the submission or in the Written Exercises; there is always a great danger that any published example will be perceived as the approved format – the 'formula for success'. This danger exists within organisations as well, where candidates may be tempted to copy an earlier successful submission in the belief that this is the way to succeed. If you are so tempted, beware of getting a nasty shock. You are an individual.

What you must do is ensure that *your* picture is complete, with each piece locked into the others and with no gaps or overlaps anywhere. It worries us when we are told, 'I've finished my Report; now I'm going to start my Presentation'. Just as with a real jigsaw we compile different groups of pieces as we recognise them, so, in our view, it is good tactics to develop all the pieces of the jigsaw together, so that they are each complete in themselves, and form a complete interlocked whole.

The jigsaws for each class of membership have the same number of pieces, with slight variations in detail.

Obviously, in the early preparation of your submission, you will not know what is going to happen at the interview, but you should, even at this early stage, have in mind what you might use for your presentation and how you might respond to the invitation to 'take us through (some other part of your experience)' informally at some point during the interview.

No Training Record

Your Training Record may have taken many years to compile, representing many years of personal development. At first, it may appear perverse (perhaps even slightly annoying) that the Reviewers do not see any of the resulting paperwork. You have, after all, put a huge amount of effort into compiling it. But the Institution has devolved the responsibility for ensuring compliance with the requirements of Initial Professional Development to your Supervising Civil Engineer (if under Agreement) or to a Career Appraisal if not. Since many engineers seem to have difficulty with this step, Chapter 3 covers this critical preliminary stage of the process, although it is not specifically part of a successful Review.

Throughout your preparation for Review, keep in mind the overriding shift of emphasis:

Have you, as a result of what you have experienced, developed the attributes of a professional engineer?

The emphasis at the Review has switched away from 'How did you become a professional engineer?' to 'Have you become one?'. This removes undue reliance on any training system or quality of experience, and places the emphasis very firmly on the outcome, in line with the Engineering Council, which requires 'an increased focus on output standards' (EC, 2010). The Reviewers will:

review the product of training, not the process of training.

What all that training documentation ought to have done, however, is to have allowed you to:

- develop the skills, knowledge and understanding you now need to be successful
- develop a methodology and attitude which will stand you in good stead as you set about writing the submission documents for the Review.

Subsequent chapters of this book consider each piece of the jigsaw in turn and how it interlocks with others, but the first of these, Chapter 4, spends some time looking at the completed jigsaw – the picture on the lid of the box containing all the pieces.

Time to prepare for the Review?

The Professional Review is the culmination of many years' work and personal development, which started long before you went to university or college. It is the point at which many strands of development are brought together – technical knowledge, professional responsibility, personal characteristics – to demonstrate and prove your competence to fulfil the role of a professional engineer within your particular field of expertise. It is most certainly not an examination of whether you are capable of doing your current job, which is unfortunately how many unsuccessful candidates (and some of their sponsors) seem to view it.

So, one answer to the question of how long it should take to prepare is 'Many years'. In reality, however, we hope you are continually reviewing your progress against defined targets – the Attribute descriptions of what has to be demonstrated at the Review.

There will come a point (usually quite suddenly) when you feel confident about your ability – that is the moment to start preparing the submission. From this moment, and based on watching many candidates, we recommend a minimum period of six months before the submission date. On this basis, a rough programme would be:

Submission by	Reports drafted by	Sponsors approached by	Supporting documents by
February	End of September	End of November	End of January
August	End of March	End of May	End of July
End of June (non-UK)	Mid-February	Mid-April	Mid-June

Such a programme incorporates adequate leeway for time lags in responses from your sponsors and advisers and allows for delays caused by holidays. But it still means that preparation has to be pursued diligently and constantly if the submission is to be of the highest standard, demonstrating your capabilities to best advantage. We have known successful candidates who started long after the dates suggested above, but they virtually abandoned everything else in a frantic surge of 'accelerated working'. One of Mac's graduates even managed the entire document preparation in a weekend (but he had been discussing the contents with Mac for weeks beforehand).

In addition to the preparation of the submission documents, you will also have to programme into your schedule the preparation for the interview (including a presentation) and the written work. It seems that few young engineers 'acquire an appreciation of broad industry and society related topics' in the normal course of their work or by research and reading around their profession, so it is usually tackled like some kind of crash course at the end. We deprecate this, but acknowledge that this is the reality of most situations. But do not underestimate the work involved. It is unlikely to be successfully squeezed into the period between the submission and the interview.

Successful Professional Reviews for Civil Engineers
ISBN 978-0-7277-6100-2

http://dx.doi.org/10.1680/sprce61002.011

Chapter 3
Career Appraisal (CA)

This preliminary step towards the Professional Review is 'a way for you to complete the initial professional development (IPD) stage ... of your professional qualification'. It is a requirement for all but the Technical Report route. For those who have completed a Training Agreement, the specification is the same but, of course, your Supervising Civil Engineer (SCE) has by this stage got to know you and your capabilities well, so formal completion should not involve much additional work. The advice in this chapter may, however, still be of use to you and your SCE in making sure you are on the right track.

The Institution tells you exactly what you need to do for a CA in its publication *Career Appraisal Guidance*. The following expands on that advice as a result of our experiences, as SCEs, Reviewers and as Appraisers of CA submissions.

With the CA, the Institution is acting as a surrogate SCE. We have come across a mistaken belief among a few graduates that the CA route is a means of avoiding writing regular reports of their career progress. We can assure them that the written evidence needed for a successful CA is far more onerous for the following reasons:

- You are faced with a 'one-stop shop' rather than a progressive accumulation over several years.
- The Appraisers will not meet you and certainly don't know you. All of the evidence must be presented cold; convincing someone who has never met you and who does not know what responsibilities you have been carrying is far more difficult.
- Much of what you have done and learnt has already receded to the back of your mind, even in this relatively short period of experience. The only time you realise that something is new to you is the very first time you experience it. After that it becomes commonplace or 'obvious' and, as a result, there is difficulty in recalling it.

The simplest route to professional qualification has always been via a conscientiously pursued Training Agreement with a good SCE, where some effort is applied steadily and regularly over an extended period, rather than squashed into preparation for a CA. Not everyone, however, gets the chance of a Training Agreement, so the CA is their only formal mentoring support, a substitute provided by the ICE.

This CA step is not an obstacle but an opportunity for you to gain advice and counsel on how close you are to successfully applying for a Professional Review. The CA will do two things:

- look back to see whether you have had adequate opportunities to fulfil each of the Attribute requirements to the required level (A, K, E)
- look forward to see whether or not you are likely to be able to demonstrate how that experience has benefitted you in becoming a professional engineer. To aid in this process, you are asked to provide an Experience Report. While this will undoubtedly be the basis upon which your Professional Review Report for the Review itself will be prepared, this version does not have quite the same objectives.

The mentor

The Institution advises that the first step is to find an experienced civil engineer to act as your mentor. There are few restrictions on whom this might be but, if possible, it 'should be a member of the ICE'. We believe this is imperative if at all possible, because they really should be familiar with the ICE's qualification processes and grades of membership. Further, they should also be up to date with current standards and the interpretation of the Attributes, since it is likely that these were introduced after they themselves became members. The most obvious mentor, if they are willing, is a current SCE, either from within your own organisation or someone you know and who is prepared to assist you professionally. Your Regional Support Team may be able to help identify a willing, experienced engineer if you are really stuck.

There is no doubt that, although you can self-certify your achievements, getting your Attributes endorsed by a competent mentor does add credibility. But the responsibility remains yours. Do not put your mentor in a situation where their professional credibility is called into question due to your poor submission.

The CA submission documents

You are required to submit your CA documents electronically to the Institution. The required documents are:

- application form (obtained from the ICE website)
- certified copies of your academic qualifications
- a detailed CV
- a completed Appendix A of the ICE document *Career Appraisal Guidance*
- an Experience Report
- other, *cross-referenced*, documents such as appendices (our emphasis)
- continuing professional development records.

12

File submission rules

Your Career Appraisal submission must:

■ comprise one self-contained PDF file
■ be A4 sized (but A3 allowed for a maximum of three drawings)
■ contain a maximum of 12 pages of additional information, including any relevant calculations
■ be no larger than 10MB
■ have a filename as specified by the Institution (at the time of writing, 2015, this is to be your ICE member number, initials, surname and review date – for example, 12345678_J.GILES_17.10.15).

The Institution's document, *Career Appraisal Guidance*, offers some useful advice on how to develop your file and it is worth repeating here:

■ Include hyperlinks to link data in the appendices with the relevant text in your report.
■ Use colour where necessary – for example, for images and drawings.
■ Where possible, convert individual documents to PDF electronically, rather than by scanning them.
■ Include hyperlinks to the appendices where possible.
■ Ensure that the file is printable in the correct format.
■ Use an appropriate font and text size.

We have experience of appraising CAs and some common themes stand out from previous appraisals. It helps if your submission is well-presented. However, do not go to great trouble to produce a really high quality finish, as you might for a client; neat and tidy, with the minimum of fancy covers and extraneous pages, in 10, 11 or 12pt font is perfectly acceptable.

Lists of contents and comprehensive indices are less useful than the relevant documents being inserted directly following each Attribute, cross-referenced locally rather than within the whole document.

Do not use your employer's standard corporate documentation covers. The process is about you, not your employer.

The Appraisers, like the Reviewers, are only too well aware that the name of your employer is not a reliable indicator of the specific quality of your training and experience, so do not flaunt it. Remember too, that use of official logos may contravene the policies of both your employer and the Institution.

Some submissions are very much larger than others, although the file size limit may now encourage succinct documents. Generally speaking, the larger ones are found to be badly targeted, where the candidate has submitted everything which might possibly be relevant, in the hope that the Appraisers will find what they are looking for. This is annoying and might prove counter-productive as the Appraisers may not be prepared to spend a long time searching and may draw adverse conclusions about the applicant's ability to communicate.

Shorter submissions usually show that the applicant has thought carefully about the relevance and value of each piece of evidence, and has submitted 'just enough'. A really good submission uses one piece of work to demonstrate achievement of several Attributes and thus further reduces the reading time needed. At the Review, you are required to *demonstrate* your competence; the Reviewers are not obliged to tease it out, either from your submitted documents or at interview. So, compiling a compact set of documents, every word of which is relevant to the CA, is good practice.

Attributes

There are three progressive levels of achievement – **K**nowledge of, **E**xperience in and **A**bility to – for each Attribute. To compile a 'progressive record', you will record when and how you achieved each level, using the forms in Appendix A of the ICE publication *Career Appraisal Guidance*. You will have appreciated that some of the Attributes exist very soon after starting your degree course, and **K**now about them as soon as you applied that initial awareness in worked examples. So, you should be able to complete many of the Date Achieved boxes for **K** very quickly, using the university's syllabus and any worked examples as evidence.

We do not believe you can go further as an undergraduate because **E**xperience is commensurate with responsibility. Your prime target at university is to get the best degree you can; there is no long-term responsibility. Only in the workplace will you truly become responsible for the safety and well-being of people, use of scarce resources and protection of the environment.

So, **E**xperience dates will reflect your first involvement in that aspect in the workplace. When does this translate to **A**bility, as we have been asked by many trainees and mentors over the years? We believe that the criterion is fulfilled when you are able to resolve *any* problem which might arise in your particular work section. This does not mean that you could necessarily resolve the problem yourself, but that you would know the appropriate person to whom to delegate it, or even decide that it was beyond the resources of your work group and refer it somewhere else. This latter action would be a very clear example of 'identify the limits of your own personal knowledge and skills'.

Remember that there are two places, both limited but operating in tandem, in which to demonstrate the achievement levels: the space marked 'Achievement' under each Attribute, and your Experience Report. Integrate the two judiciously without repetition to maximise your evidence.

Experience Report (ER)

The ICE requires a report of not more than 2000 words in length, cross-referenced to the Attributes, which must include a brief statement of your proposed route onwards to a Professional Review. The objectives of your ER are to:

■ amplify, by cross-referencing, how the Attributes have been achieved. The report is useful to your Appraisers because it gives chronological continuity to the Attributes. This also provides an opportunity for you to expand further on how each one was achieved, so the two documents (Attributes and ER) should be prepared together to make sure there are no overlaps but that there is integrated conformity

■ give a 'brief statement of your proposed route onwards to a Professional Review'. Towards the end of the report, we suggest you indicate how you intend to develop the Experience Report into the Professional Development Report to demonstrate the Attributes you have developed, and give your target date and membership grade for the Review.

There is a statement in the *Career Appraisal Guidance* that the report 'can be modified, updated, and expanded before being included in your review submission'. This is because the objectives of the Professional Review Report submission are different, but much of the information in Chapters 10, 11 and 12 on the Professional Review Report is just as relevant here:

■ Present the facts of your career in the Foreword to leave you with as many words as possible to describe the outcomes for your professional development.

■ You need succinct explanations, not of what you did, but of how and why you did it. Whenever you write sentences beginning with things like, 'I managed the office resources' or 'I monitored the expenditure' stop to think what that means to someone who has no idea what you were doing. Did you merely put the kettle on (it is, after all, an office resource) or watch while the expenditure went several times over budget?

■ Always presume that the reader knows nothing and try to read your words through their eyes. You and your mentors fully understand what you mean by what you have written, but it may not be apparent at all to your Appraisers.

The simplest way to cross-reference the Attributes is by annotating the report in the margin with the number and level of achievement (e.g. 5A'K').

Continuing Professional Development (CPD)

There is a whole chapter of this book (Chapter 9) devoted to CPD for the Reviews, the content of which is equally applicable to a CA. The minima quoted by the ICE are, in our experience, very low. Most of the graduates we have worked with and met are easily exceeding these minimum requirements. It was always the recording (the quality assurance) which presented the difficulty. Of necessity, we all learn constantly throughout our careers, at no time faster than when we first join the industry. Most of you will have had some sort of induction training, sometimes over several days; most of the material transmitted during that training is CPD, so record it.

You should have no difficulty at all in complying with at least the minimum requirements, provided that you keep good records. Do re-visit the Institution guidance on its website to remind yourself of the huge range of activities which can count towards your professional development, provided you record the benefit you gained.

Timing

The Institution advises candidates to allow four months between receiving the result of a CA and the submission for Review. It also states that you should allow eight weeks from the application cut-off date of the fifteenth of each month for your result. So, presuming you get your CA submission in at the beginning of a month and everything goes well, the minimum period before submitting for Review must be six months, i.e. you should aim to submit for a CA on the submission dates for the Reviews six months prior to your targeted date.

The outcome

You cannot 'fail' a CA; you can only be deferred pending certain action, which does not incur additional fees. The Institution may request additional documentary evidence to satisfy the Appraisers that a certain aspect of your experience is adequate. This does not necessarily mean that you do not have the necessary experience, merely that you have not told them about it. But they may have uncovered a weakness in some aspect of your experience which needs attention before such evidence can be produced. So, it could be some weeks or months before you are able to send the additional evidence.

Sometimes the Appraisers will refer you to the ICE's local Regional Support Team, and may write to them to provide more details of their concerns. Do take advantage of these offers, which are genuine attempts to assist you to be successful.

If your Appraisers are reasonably satisfied with the level and extent of your demonstrated experience, the Institution will send you a letter by email that you may proceed with an application for Professional Review. There will be at least one proviso: apply only when you consider (and your sponsors confirm) that you can demonstrate how this experience has enabled you to develop the Attributes required, at the grade for which you intend to apply. This reinforces the distinction between the objectives of the CA and of the Review. The first tries to ensure that you have had adequate experience, from which you should have been able to develop the qualities of a professional engineer. The second requires you to demonstrate that you really have developed the Attributes and can apply them.

The letter may also comment on perceived minor shortfalls in your experience or offer guidance on how you should proceed. This advice is valuable and should be taken seriously, so discuss any comments with your mentors and sponsors. The Appraisers are not being obstructive, but wish to ensure that you stand a good chance of success.

Successful Professional Reviews for Civil Engineers
ISBN 978-0-7277-6100-2

ICE Publishing: All rights reserved
http://dx.doi.org/10.1680/sprce61002.019

Chapter 4
The complete picture

Before considering the detail of the 'picture on the jigsaw box', it is important to think about the underlying purpose of the Reviews. This is not some sort of one-stop examination, for which you can cram and swot and then forget what you have memorised a day later. It is a *review* of the benefits you have gained from the experience you have had and an assessment of whether these benefits have developed the required attitude, understanding and skills – it is

a review of what you have become, not of what you have done.

Obviously, one cannot truly be separated from the other, but the focus is very definitely on you, not your work. Your experience and specific projects are the vehicles by which you demonstrate your abilities; they will not, in themselves, impress the Reviewers. There is no automatic correlation between the prestige or complexity of the work and the benefits you gained. Some people can have excellent experience but do not take full advantage of it. At the other extreme, some people have access to limited experience, but make maximum use of it to develop the requisite knowledge, skills and understanding.

Despite the best efforts of the Institution, there still appears to be widespread misunderstanding, exemplified by comments we continue to hear, about the purpose of the Reviews. There is nothing mystical about the Reviews; the present system is the culmination of well over 70 years' experience in the review process. Further changes will be made as more operational experience is gained and as the competencies being reviewed become more clearly defined. However, three problems will always be inherent:

(*a*) The personal qualities and understanding being sought are intangible and therefore difficult to define.

This is the reason why there are complaints that the Institution keeps 'moving the goalposts'. We do not think it does. Fundamentally, the Institution was seeking substantially the same abilities and understanding when we submitted as it is today, even though the descriptor words may be different. Engineering is like 'management'; if there were only one agreed definition for all time, there would not be so many books on it. The requirements are not static; they shift as the demands on our profession change.

(b) Young engineers, dominated by (and highly proficient in) very structured examination systems during their formal education, will always seek syllabuses, model submissions and defined targets. None of these can be produced.

Candidates familiar with comprehensive academic syllabuses can be flummoxed by the lack of guidance and rules for the Review. The Institution offers a general statement of what must be demonstrated, but little or no guidance on how to demonstrate it – it is a performance specification rather than a method specification.

So candidates seek precedents; examining what others have done to be successful. Hence, the creation of all the myths about the experience required, and what the Reviewers expect, all of which may be well-meaning, but misguided and restrictive. For the same reasons, many candidates try to emulate someone else's successful submission – this won't work, because every individual engineer is different and their experience is unique, even if they are working with others on the same projects in the same office.

(c) This is a review, not an examination. A review of your capabilities, some of which you may not yet have had an opportunity to utilise.

At the time of the Review, candidates are in a 'chicken and egg' situation – 'I believe I have become a professional engineer, but I am not doing a professional engineer's job yet because I am not qualified as a professional engineer'. So, to some extent, the Reviewers are measuring potential. Fundamentally, they are seeking an attitude: an attitude towards the management of technical, economic and environmental risks, based on a thorough understanding of the principles behind them. The development of this attitude will obviously vary dependent on age, available experience and responsibility to date, requiring the Reviewers to make a judgement. It is a judgement of the whole person, your capabilities and understanding, not an assessment of all the disparate details; what is known as the 'holistic review'.

The holistic review

The Review process is described by the Institution as 'holistic', a word which is more usually associated with alternative medicine and ecology. It comes from 'holism' – the belief that the whole is greater than the sum of its parts. The Reviewers are encouraged to concern themselves with the whole of your capability, rather than analysing each separate part in detail. Their training emphasises the interdependence of the various qualities being sought, in the context of your particular work environment, and the need to make a judgement about your overall capability. An examiner for the UK driving test says that the examiners are told to sit through the test, and decide at the end whether the person is safe or not. If that decision is 'No', then they have to think through why they made that 'instinctive' judgement and list the reasons. A very similar methodology is used by your Reviewers. Their first question when you leave them could be summarised as, 'Is this candidate safe to let loose on an unsuspecting public?'. After all, you could put a brass plate on your door and be a sole practitioner the day after you get the successful result.

There is no weighting; one part of the Review is not more important than any other; no one Attribute takes precedence over any other.

However, adequacy in every Attribute is unlikely to be enough. You must demonstrate that you have more to offer in some areas; the median is not the minimum, but is well above it.

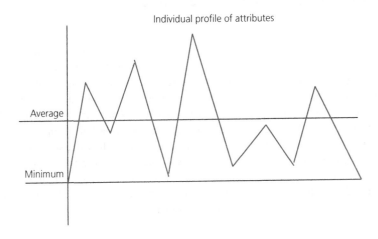

Individual profile of attributes

The Attributes which pull the average up are specific to you, based on your social background, education, available experience and personal preferences. No two profiles will ever be the same.

This means that it is possible (and it *has* actually happened) that while one aspect may have been found less than acceptable, the person has satisfied the Reviewers that, overall, they are perfectly capable of discharging the responsibilities of a Member in their particular circumstances. We recommend you ensure that you demonstrate that you are adequate in every respect.

Each individual profile will be different across the range of Attributes, but the average is the same for all.

The fundamental problems of the submission

We believe that there are fundamental, deep-rooted problems inherent in the whole process. These difficulties need to be addressed by every candidate as they start to think about the preparation of a submission:

Personal opinions

For years, engineers, even when studying science back at school, were taught to write in the third person: 'Such-and-such was decided' or 'It was agreed that...'. Now you are required to write in the first person: 'I decided' or 'In my opinion, it might have been better if...'. The Reviews require you to demonstrate that you have become a professional engineer, not just list the experience you have had. So you *must* write about yourself and your personal opinions, which goes against everything you have been taught. Engineers do not like writing about themselves, particularly for the scrutiny of two strangers; we find it embarrassing. Do not underestimate this problem; it is a significant hurdle in the preparation of a good submission.

Self-confidence

Civil engineers are in the business of risk management, which is always a matter of judgement, and so we do not boast. We are rarely, if ever, certain that our decisions are absolute. How can they be, when the parameters are constantly changing? We like to talk through problems and solutions to confirm that we have solved them correctly – a trait which offers a huge potential benefit to entrants to our profession: to learn through discussion. Experienced engineers actually derive benefit from revisiting and reiterating the arguments they went through in arriving at their decisions and both of us are aware of occasions where such a dialogue altered our perceptions. If confronted (for example, in a court of law), we rarely, if ever, say 'Yes' or 'No' without some qualification – 'Yes, perhaps...' or 'No, but...'. At Review you are required to show that you are decisive and able to inspire confidence in others.

Own responsibility

We all know that we do not work in isolation but are part of teams. As a result, we are loathe to take credit for our personal decisions, knowing that they have usually been discussed with many people before implementation. The result is that we write 'We decided' or 'A decision was made'. But who would take the blame if, subsequently, these decisions were found to be incorrect? If it is you then, no matter how many people you discussed it with, it is *your* decision – 'I decided...'.

Assessing others' decisions

By and large, at the time you present for Review, you are still working at a relatively low level in the hierarchy. In many organisations, and in certain cultures, it is not acceptable, if you wish to progress, to openly question decisions taken by more senior engineers. But the Reviewers will *expect* you to have views on how high-level decisions were made. In the future, you might be expected to take similar decisions as a qualified professional engineer, and you must demonstrate that you have that ability. Your opinions can be couched in terms which do not suggest criticism, but rather curiosity and a desire to understand. Senior managers surely cannot take offence at that.

Demonstrating understanding

Most people coming up to Professional Review have progressed through many years of education – at school, college and/or university. They have developed many techniques to successfully negotiate detailed syllabuses, coursework and, particularly, examinations. If you attempt to use the same techniques for the Professional Review, they probably will not work.

The Review is not an examination.

It is an assessment of whether you have developed enough skill and understanding to operate as a professional engineer. Obviously, these qualities are dependent on having some knowledge but, unlike most examinations, the Review is not primarily a test of knowledge but a test of your understanding. An examination largely tests your ability to recall knowledge and apply it to resolve problems similar to those you encountered during your course. There is usually a definitive answer. At the Review, the questions will be framed in such a way that you are unlikely to be able to give an answer – they will be so-called 'open' questions, enabling you to discuss the subject and thus demonstrate your understanding.

At Review, the Reviewers are continually asking the question, 'Would this person, when placed in a position of responsibility, make the right decisions?' (note: 'Would they', not 'Have they'). In other words, you may not yet have had the opportunities to put your capability into practice. This concept of capability is, at first, difficult to comprehend, but must be grasped if a successful Review is to be the outcome.

Successful Professional Reviews for Civil Engineers
ISBN 978-0-7277-6100-2

ICE Publishing: All rights reserved
http://dx.doi.org/10.1680/sprce61002.025

Chapter 5
Professional engineer

Mac's earlier book, *Effective Training for Civil Engineers*, included four 'definitions' of a Chartered Engineer and three of an Incorporated Engineer, all dating back to publications from the Engineering Council, the Fédération Européenne d'Associations Nationales d'Ingénieurs and our Institution (the Chilver Report) from the 1970s. So there was nothing new in them – Mac merely brought them together. The Council of the Institution published another set of descriptions in 1998, while the introduction of the ICE 3000 series brought yet another version, which is substantially the same as is in use from 2015. In fact, engineers have been attempting to 'define' themselves since long before Henry Palmer and Thomas Tredgold in 1828 – even Aristotle had a go!

We all seem to remember Tredgold's 'the Art of directing the great sources of Power in Nature for the use and convenience of Man' but of more relevance today is another part of our Charter, added in 1972:

> calls for a high degree of professional knowledge and judgement in making the best use of scarce resources in care for the environment and in the interests of public health and safety.

This description of our role is well worth remembering; it could be useful in many of the answers to the written part of the Review.

We have a collection of 'definitions' from all over the world; all are trying to say the same thing, but none is a 'prescription'. If there were an easy definition, then all the prolific writers on management, let alone engineering management, would have long since run out of ideas. As many Reviewers have said over the years, 'We know one when we see one', but no one can decisively define a Professional Engineer.

The only relevant currently available information for candidates is Appendix A – Table of Attributes in the ICE's *Professional Review Guidance*, which encapsulates the whole specification for the Reviews. Every part of your effort so far should have had these Attributes in mind – your experience, training, Continuing Professional Development (CPD). Even if, up to now, your understanding was a little vague, preparation of the submission documents, as well as your preparation for the interview and any Written

Exercise, must now focus exclusively on demonstrating these nine Attributes and how you developed them.

Having said that, we believe the purpose of the Reviews can be summarised in two sentences:

- Do you fully understand what you are doing?
- Do you understand the full implications of what you are doing?

For a Technician Member, there is far less emphasis on the second of these sentences, while, at the other end of the spectrum, there is considerable emphasis on the wider understanding and full implications of your role when you are applying to become a Chartered Member.

Deciding whether you have become a professional engineer

Many engineers, both candidates and senior managers, have still not come to terms with the fact that the Member Professional Review (MPR) encompasses what many older engineers demonstrated when they became Chartered Members. There is now a greater expectation of a thorough understanding of the whole procurement process at the Chartered Professional Review (CPR), well beyond technical competence and management. Yet, still, too many CPR candidates come forward demonstrating the attitude and understanding of an Incorporated Engineer, despite both the Institution's and the Engineering Council's best efforts.

There is now the opportunity to use this attitude and understanding, which evolves quite quickly in the workplace (over the course of three or four years) after most Honours engineering degrees, to become a Member (IEng) as soon as possible, before the full extent of the modern Chartered Engineer's understanding has been gained. If successful, you will subsequently be required to show only the differences between the grades through the progressive route at a later date when you have had appropriate further experience and apply for Chartered status.

But even now, we still occasionally hear that 'you need a design for your civils', that 'you need twelve months on site/in design', that 'you need a bill of quantities and a rate build-up', that 'you can only count civils meetings if you have written 500-word reports', that you need to perambulate around all the departments in an organisation before a Training Agreement can be signed off. None of these is a requirement of the Institution. You may have done some, any or all for your personal development, it might be a good idea, your SCE may insist, but they are not *requirements* –

there are very few 'rules' on how you develop.

The requirement is that, at the Review, you

demonstrate that you have achieved the required skills and understanding as defined by Appendix A.

What is required is that, by some means or other, you gain adequate experience to develop the characteristics being sought. The Review seeks to evaluate the outcome of training, and is not particularly interested in the process. This is why your Training Record, so laboriously compiled, forms no part of the Review.

The end product is 'defined' (albeit very loosely), but not the precise means of achieving it. Of themselves, minimal achievement of the Attributes will not be enough, but they do form a solid framework upon which 'responsible experience' can be built. There can be no specification for your personal development, because everybody starts from a different point and has different innate abilities, education and experience (even if working in the same office). The manner in which you undertake Initial Professional Development is dependent on your motivation and background and the experience available.

Work experience needed

We can assure you, having watched many engineers progress successfully through the Reviews, that it is possible to gain adequate experience in the most unexpected situations. No longer does the Institution have routes for so-called specialists; the reality is that

every candidate is a specialist

whether in design or construction, feasibility or demolition, concrete, steel or masonry, bitumens, geotextiles, groundwater movement, coastal protection, oil, traffic calming, public transport, even as far removed as insurance assessment and actuarial work, but all must be able to display the skills and understanding required.

Some trainees we meet have never had the opportunity for a Training Agreement. For some, employment consists of a series of temporary contracts (some of only a few months' duration) with organisations not on the ICE Index of Employers Approved for Training. Yet they can have exemplary Training Records. How? Because the purpose of training and the required end result were fully understood and senior people have been cajoled into assisting. Their records contain a complete set of critically annotated reports, a ratified set of achieved Attributes (formerly Objectives) and more than adequate confirmed CPD. Furthermore, all the required abilities are evident, both in their submission documents and at Review.

These examples imply that all the information needed *is* available – but still the hearsay and half-truths persist. It is difficult to understand why, except that many people seem far more comfortable with a set of rules or boxes which can be ticked off as complete, thus avoiding the need for judgement and assessment against a series of rather vague criteria.

What you must do is continually drive yourself, with the assistance of your mentors, around the cycle:

assess yourself against the end-product – identify any deficiencies
seek experience or off-the-job training – rectify any shortcomings.

Successful Professional Reviews for Civil Engineers
ISBN 978-0-7277-6100-2

ICE Publishing: All rights reserved
http://dx.doi.org/10.1680/sprce61002.029

Chapter 6
The Review specification

Expansion of the Appendix A tables

Looking initially at those items in Appendix A of *Professional Review Guidance*, they do not seem too onerous. However, once you start trying to demonstrate your ability in each of them, they become far less clear. Like all specifications, they should be read with the intention of finding out how best to comply (i.e. achieve the performance). But this is not straightforward, particularly if you have become used to detailed syllabuses during education and are now using detailed specifications at work, many of which leave you little room for manoeuvre. Do not fall into the trap of wondering what the Institution expects; the straight answer is that neither it nor the Reviewers know. There are so many ways and means of demonstrating capability in each Attribute that only you and your close advisers can decide what is best suited to you. This versatility is one of the great strengths of the Institution's Review process and should be used to your advantage.

It is useful to reflect on how the criteria are being interpreted. We have taken each section in turn and amplified it in the context of other documents concerning the responsibilities of professional civil engineers, issued by the Institution and other professional bodies, and in the light of our experience with, and as, Reviewers. But these interpretations are just that – our interpretations – and you, as a candidate, should think the problem through for yourself, hopefully with the co-operation of your mentors and by reading up-to-date Institution policy published on the website.

You have, of course, been following a training scheme, whether formal or not, so by now you must have developed, with the help of your mentors, some understanding of how to use your experience to demonstrate the Attributes. Your training period, whether formally under agreement or not, should have ensured that you have had adequate experience to be able to develop the required qualities.

What you must now do is to edit the evidence of that experience which you have compiled to present the best possible demonstration of your skills and abilities to the Reviewers. This is unlikely to be in the format of the Attributes: although there is nothing in the rules to stop such an approach, the experience may well become disjointed and difficult for your Reviewers to follow, while the need to detail several pieces of experience to demonstrate each Attribute will probably use too many of the available words, leaving you with too few to explain the benefit you gained.

The Institution's Attributes have not been developed in isolation. They are based on the UK Engineering Council's Attributes, to which all of its licensed bodies must adhere. Although some of the Engineering Council's generic Attributes (see www.engc.org.uk) differ from those of the Institution, it is worth looking at them, if only because they include a column to help candidates 'identify activities which you might quote to demonstrate the required competence', with the important proviso that 'these are not exhaustive'. The Institution staff may be able to offer some more suggestions. As more Review experience becomes available, there will inevitably be greater certainty of interpretation, so check that you have the latest information before you start compiling your evidence for Review.

All of the following paragraphs are numbered and most are lettered to relate to the Attributes set out in Appendix A for your particular class of membership. Each section includes MICE (IEng and CEng), and the progressive route from IEng to CEng (CPRP). There is an implication in paragraph A1.2 that even where your academic qualifications do not satisfy the Engineering Council, the same Attributes apply and you must 'demonstrate a sound understanding of core engineering principles' in the fields in which you work to become an Associate (AMICE).

1. Knowledge and understanding of engineering

A. Engineering knowledge is an understanding of the theoretical properties of materials and the basic behaviour of engineering systems (i.e. the technical principles of strength of materials, soil mechanics, hydraulics, structures and the many other subjects covered during your formal education as a civil engineer). ICE Reviewers become concerned whenever, for example, a candidate is unable to draw simple bending moment or shear force diagrams for structures they have analysed, or to state the basic formulae upon which their calculations of flow rates in pipes are based. If, for example, you have used a programme dependent on Young's modulus to check possible deflections, or software based on Darcy's law to estimate groundwater movements, then surely it is a prerequisite that you know what they are and how the software developer has used them? Yet both of us have interviewed candidates who patently did not.

The same reasoning applies to other processes of analysis you may use, for example statistical probability theory, the biological and chemical principles of remediation or decomposition or any of the scientific principles on which your work relies. If you have estimated groundwater movements, or made estimates of future traffic flows based on limited samples of the existing situation, or predicted the effects of an earthquake, then surely it is a prerequisite that you understand the principles behind your statistical analyses? This will certainly be the expectation of your Reviewers.

A clear understanding of the fundamental properties of matter and the basic theory behind the processes of analysis you choose to use ensures that existing and emerging technology is properly applied. This fundamental knowledge enables you to:

- correctly apply appropriate technology, particularly software, where it is important to identify what assumptions are inherent in the program and to then determine whether or not those assumptions are valid in the case of your particular problem
- check the results generated by sophisticated programs by some rudimentary calculations – quick methods based on technical principles – to make sure that the results are of the correct order of magnitude
- develop the imagination to anticipate possible scenarios and the understanding to make sensible judgements about suitability, risk and the proper use of resources.

B. For both classes of membership, you are expected not only to utilise existing technology properly by seeking the necessary evidence, but also to demonstrate how you strive to improve and advance it. So mere compliance will not be enough: you will be expected to talk at interview about possible improvements which could be introduced, whether they have been considered by your employer or not.

C–D. In addition, for the Chartered Professional Review, you must demonstrate that you are able to use your understanding of engineering principles as the basis for both developing and exploiting new technology in innovative ways. This requires you to keep up to date with ongoing developments in your particular field which may have relevance to your work and demonstrate that you seek to introduce them where appropriate.

2. Technical and practical application of engineering

A–C. On a superficial reading, this Attribute group does seem to partially overlap with group 1. Engineering application is the ability to apply established analytical methods and procedures appropriately, something which requires a thorough understanding of the principles upon which those procedures rely. However, 'procedures' are not restricted to technical analysis, but include all those systems used for the management and control of the tasks undertaken by the organisation.

Further consideration reveals that this group also covers the application of principles as part of the whole solution to a problem. The Reviewers seek a wider perspective, where candidates can demonstrate that they are able to choose the optimum techniques, procedures and methods – what is often referred to as *appropriate technology* – fitting the means to the end. Blindly following existing practice within your own organisation is not a justification for doing anything unless you can demonstrate that there is a reason why something has always been done in a certain way. So, as a simple example, what might be appropriate in an environment where labour is cheap might not be suitable in another place where wages are relatively high. A sophisticated analytical technique producing a complex high-tech solution might not be appropriate in a developing country. Safe working conditions may differ radically from one country to another, depending on the perceived value of human life.

D. At every stage of an engineering solution, from identifying the parameters of a problem, through the implementation of a solution to the maintenance and eventual modification or demolition, engineers are required to ensure that those following them in the progression can carry out their part of the process safely and effectively; it is totally unacceptable, for example, to say, as one of our candidates did, 'I don't know. That is the contractor's problem!'.

C&F. It is a requirement that candidates have taken part in the implementation of engineering solutions (whether they involve conventional construction or not) and considered how successful they have been. Candidates must have developed, as a direct consequence of their involvement, opinions and views regarding whether the solution is appropriate, effective and provides the best possible outcome.

E. There is a requirement to evaluate the effectiveness of solutions. To look back and gather that great learning experience for all engineers – hindsight! To watch the maintenance and operation of the solution and determine what might have been done better or more effectively. Only then can better solutions be devised in the future. So do not be surprised during your interview if a Reviewer asks questions such as, 'Was that the best way to do it?', 'Would you do it the same way again?' or 'If you are inspecting this structure in 30 years' time, where do you think the problems might be?'. Almost always, hindsight will suggest a better way of resolving a problem.

3. Management and leadership

Management is defined as 'guiding and directing functions, resources and people within the context of a given project or activity'. There is, in our view, a distinct difference between management ('guiding and directing') and supervision ('controlling'). Supervision is about telling people what to do and how to do it, leaving precious little space for them to use their own initiative. Good management requires the replacement of direct control with mutual trust and personal responsibility: a difficult but rewarding transition for both employee and manager.

A. Effective project implementation requires you to develop your own self-management. Starting out in the workplace can seem like being caught under an unending avalanche, with no pause for thought. Work just pours in and you are expected to juggle several jobs at once. Your managers will presume that you are able to cope, but few new employees can, without some basic guidance and support.

B. Prioritising work, management of time and people, and staying calm under pressure are all things you probably have to learn from hard experience, sometimes with formal or informal guidance. You should demonstrate that you have such capabilities by examples in any submission (whether for CEng or IEng). Do not be surprised if the Reviewers ask you to tell them about 'something which gave you a sleepless night'.

C. Management is directing people towards the outcome which needs to be achieved and, perhaps, providing guidance on how it might be accomplished. Approaching the Member Professional Review, you should no longer need to be supervised, and ought to be taking more responsibility, having developed the knowledge and confidence to accept it. You must demonstrate that you can manage yourself and others in your team effectively, as well as being capable of obtaining the necessary resources (such as time, equipment and knowledge) for the team to achieve the required outcome.

D. And all of this must be in the context of satisfying quality processes. Most, if not all organisations now have systems for the routine monitoring and control of quality, but mere compliance with such systems will not be enough to satisfy your Reviewers. You will be expected to have views on systems' effectiveness and appropriateness, as well as suggestions regarding whether you think they might be improved, and how.

E. To become a Chartered Member, you are required to be capable of leading activities and change. Leadership is defined by the ICE as being capable of 'setting the direction of a project or activity and encouraging and guiding people towards that direction'. This agrees with the Leadership Trust definition: 'Leadership is using one's own personal power to win the hearts and minds of people to achieve a common purpose'.

F. Leadership is not a function of your position, but a desire to persuade people of the validity of a course of action which you envisage. It is as visible in a primary school playground as in higher management, and must be demonstrated to the Reviewers, even where you might consider that you are not yet in a position of leadership within the hierarchy of your organisation or, indeed, if you are self-employed.

To become a Chartered Engineer, you must demonstrate that

- you have successfully challenged others to progress their abilities to meet new challenges
- you have encouraged them to work beyond areas where they have previously felt comfortable
- you have a vision of what you want to change, where you want to improve, and that you can inspire others to achieve that end.

Leadership is about personality and a willingness to take calculated risks – being prepared to 'put yourself on the line', motivating and inspiring others to follow you.

The ideal employee's abilities straddle the requirements of both management and leadership but there is undoubtedly a clear difference in personality and effective zones of influence between the two. Neither is exclusive, indeed there is considerable overlap, but there is a distinct bias for each. One tends towards routine orderliness, the other towards disruptiveness – challenging the status quo. Which one best fits you?

If you want to become a Chartered Member, you must demonstrate and explain occasions where you have managed to persuade others of the validity of your proposals and inspired them to carry the solution through. Have you ever persuaded your colleagues to stay late to meet deadlines? Have you ever changed someone's point of view?

G. You must give examples of situations where you have strived for improvements to the quality of service: for example, in the use of scarce materials or other resources, in care for the environment, in protecting the public interest or in the efficiency and safety of the solution. The fact that your proposals may not have been implemented does not matter; you have demonstrated that you are thinking about such things (though you ought to know why they were rejected).

4. Independent judgement and responsibility

A. All potential Members of the Institution must demonstrate, by examples from your experience, that at times you have felt unsure of your ability and have sought guidance from people with more experience. The responsibility for 'knowing when you don't know' is considerable and important and must be demonstrated to the Reviewers. Consider how this links to the Institution's rules of professional conduct.

B. You must demonstrate your ability to go beyond established techniques, proven methods and documented precedents to develop a solution to a problem and to take independent personal responsibility for the effectiveness of the solution. You need to demonstrate to the Reviewers that, despite being well aware of best practice as defined by Codes and Standards, there have been circumstances in which you were unable to apply it, but had to develop a compromise which, in your judgement, would work satisfactorily. That means that you took responsibility for the decision, and its possible outcomes, and are expected to be able to justify it.

C. For the Chartered Professional Review, you are additionally required to demonstrate that you can identify the limits not only of your own personal knowledge and skills, but also those of the team around you. This is a fundamental management challenge: to delegate work which your staff feel confident that they can achieve, but which at the same time presents a challenge – pushing them outside their comfort zone to develop their abilities still further.

Even where you might at first consider that you work on your own, there will inevitably be times when you are dependent on the input of others (e.g. surveys, technical or procedural expertise or marketing) and you have to make judgements on the reliability of those people and the validity of their advice. Explain how you came to your conclusions.

D. As well as demonstrating engineering judgement, show that you are capable of making wider judgements beyond solely technical matters, to achieve fine balances between such things as:

- financial costs and commercial benefits
- damage to, and benefits for, the environment
- capital investment and maintenance costs
- local disruption, health and safety and wider social benefits.

5. Commercial ability

A. Budgets are the means by which the use, control and documentation of expenditure are achieved and by which authority is delegated. Competence to prepare a budget requires you to be able to estimate the costs of doing work, the profit which needs to be achieved and, probably, how to optimise cash flow.

Budgetary control in most organisations is subject to in-house procedures, and every applicant for Review should know these procedures thoroughly and demonstrate confidence, not only in applying them, but also in using them as guidance where the particular situation is not exactly covered by the procedures. The nature of your Reviewers' interest in this type of subject will depend largely on the type of organisation(s) you have worked for.

B. Statutory and commercial frameworks include the whole legal framework within which we are required to operate, not just commercially, but technically, environmentally and socially. We consider it absolutely vital that everyone working in risk management (which is arguably what civil engineering is all about) fully understands their liabilities and duties in law. There is a proliferation of legislation in many legal jurisdictions, which shows little sign of abating, as politicians mistakenly, in our view, respond to the pressure from a blame and compensation culture. Wherever you work, you must keep yourself abreast of these developments and be prepared to discuss your perspective on them.

The development of an early understanding, and its continual updating require positive action by both yourself and your employer, probably in the form of formal training, since it could easily be too late (and expensive – or worse) if such understanding is gained by experience. At the time of writing, construction health and safety issues do seem to get this sort of critical attention, but do not be surprised if this concern is mirrored at

Review in the many other aspects of your work. Environmental and social impact, and effective use of resources, are just as important.

C. Chartered Engineers must demonstrate that they understand the balancing of costs and benefits in a professional manner to protect and benefit those to whom the organisation is responsible (e.g. clients, subcontractors, general public, staff and shareholders). They should have some knowledge about such things as equity, working capital management, forecasting and presentation of accounts (profit and loss, balance sheet and cash flow) of the organisation.

6. Health, safety and welfare

We are concerned that some of the young engineers we meet seem to think that Health and Safety (welfare is rarely thought about at all) is all about such basic things as personal protective clothing, toe boards and risk assessment form filling – particularly the latter. The emphasis placed on such material records by regulatory authorities and employers, combined with the need to combat an increasingly litigious attitude in society, has inevitably drawn attention away from the fundamental concepts to the details of compliance with rules. It is similar to treating the symptoms of an illness, rather than the illness itself. So, in this Attribute, we consider the fundamental concepts of health, safety and welfare, upon which candidates will have built an understanding based on their own experiences.

Publications from Government bodies and the Institution reinforce a 'back to basics' approach. The health, safety and welfare of everyone involved in using, visiting, maintaining, modifying and demolishing the facility, not just constructors, must be the bedrock upon which all decisions are made. These considerations constitute an attitude of mind, well beyond the humdrum details. Patrick once reviewed a candidate who had supervised the rehabilitation of water mains in busy Hong Kong streets. The candidate's explanation of the challenges of working in that environment and what he did to meet those challenges went a long way towards his Reviewers' decision to pass him.

The increasingly 'knee-jerk' responses of politicians and the public to accidents can lead to a reactive and grossly distorted waste of resources, if not tempered by the logical and pragmatic risk assessment of engineers. For example:

■ Was the widespread increase in the length of motorway safety barriers in the UK justified because one driver fell asleep and drove on to a railway line? Was that the best risk mitigation or avoidance?

■ Was the reaction to the publication of maps showing areas susceptible to flooding rational, or could the information have been publicised in a better way?

■ Is there a proven need for the proposed high speeds on HS2 and HS3 rail links in the UK, or is this merely a political desire for prestige?

Decide on your own views about your projects, but be prepared to justify them. You are not required to agree with your Reviewers, merely to explain your own thoughts in a knowledgeable manner.

Forms, procedures and online systems are the means by which this fundamental attitude and the process of assessment are recorded and communicated. Systems must never be seen as an end in themselves, but as a record of how the responsibilities are discharged.

Health
Who better than the World Health Organization to tell us what health is and what is involved in achieving it:

health comprises those aspects of human health, including quality of life, that are determined by physical, chemical, biological, social and psychosocial factors in the environment. (WHO, 1993)

This is a much wider description than most of the engineers we meet seem to realise. It is a bit wordy, but it does go on to spell out our overall responsibilities, and the need for judgements, very clearly:

[It is] the theory and practice of assessing, correcting, controlling and preventing those factors in the environment that can potentially affect adversely the health of present and future generations. (WHO, 1993)

Not a bad description of the responsibility of every civil engineer. It may be worth remembering, if only for use in the Written Exercise.

Safety
There is an attitude apparent in large sections of the public that somehow all risk can be avoided and, if it is not, then someone else must be to blame – the 'compensation culture'. The media talk of risk aversion, both in schoolchildren and in business. There are people who truly believe that the railways should never have a derailment, or that there should never be collisions on motorways. People are concerned about the risks of travelling by air or rail, but think nothing of driving on high-speed highways, which have a far greater accident risk, killing almost 2000 people annually on UK roads. Public perception is a fickle thing, and we must avoid being sucked into irrational reactions.

Safety is about *managing* risks, not trying to eliminate them, which is a lost cause anyway.

So, all candidates must be familiar with the anticipation and management of hazards and risks in investigation, design, construction, use, maintenance and demolition, within criteria defined in law or otherwise established as best practice. Obviously, the bias will be towards those parts of civil engineering in which you have had direct involvement. As a potential

Member, you are required to demonstrate that you have used your judgement in achieving acceptable situations and are prepared to defend your decisions, not merely comply with rules and procedures in an attempt to avoid blame and possible prosecution.

Welfare

This is a more nebulous concept, the 'faring well', or well-being, of everyone involved, not just constructors, but the users, maintainers and demolishers of the infrastructure being developed. The benefits cannot so easily be demonstrated. Safety (or the lack of it) can perhaps be 'measured' by a reduction in accidents, health by changes in the number of recorded days off work, but the benefits of welfare are not so clear. Yet all three are interrelated. This is now a key consideration for the stakeholders mentioned above and particularly for the designers.

Welfare overlaps considerably with health and safety, particularly when there is a serious attempt to develop a 'safety culture'. The provision of adequate and decent washrooms, toilets and catering facilities, well-decorated and spacious offices or comfortable safety and weatherproof gear which allows freedom of movement do not, of themselves, improve health and safety, but they do help to create an attitude. Offices with few, if any, external windows, no views and inadequate lighting and ventilation, do tend to generate low morale, higher staff turnover and increased sickness, contributing to the term 'sick building syndrome'. Those who have experienced the noise of working in site offices next to highway contra-flows will understand the sanctuary provided by soundproofed accommodation – not itself a safety measure, but surely contributing to a safer working environment by reducing stress.

Should we still expect site operatives to go to and from work in the same clothes as they use for work? Indeed, should washing and clothes storage places also be provided for those who exert themselves getting to work – cyclists and runners? Mac certainly found a huge jump in morale and an improved attitude of responsibility when uniforms, washing and changing facilities were provided for the staff on waste disposal sites. There were tangible improvements in health and safety, which showed themselves in less absenteeism and fewer recorded injuries. If the employer is seen to care, then it appears that the employees will respond favourably.

So do not believe that welfare is restricted to site work. It affects all aspects of infrastructure development, use, maintenance and demolition. Take note of what is being done around you, what you could do or suggest to provide a better work environment, and demonstrate your concern to your Reviewers.

Summary

As stated earlier, in a nutshell,

Do you fully understand the consequences of your work?

Those applying for Chartered Membership must additionally demonstrate that they are positively changing the attitudes of others, that they are using their vision and initiative to strive for continuous improvements in health, safety and welfare performance. Again, this does not necessarily require you to be in a position of authority; we can all influence attitudes and behaviour by example or appropriate discussion and criticism. Demonstrate that you have done so.

7. Sustainable development

In this Attribute, we have again resorted to discussing the fundamental concepts to give candidates a feel for how each individual may satisfy the criteria and their Reviewers' expectations.

Sustainable development is the pragmatic response to the theoretical concept of sustainability. It is the management of resources in a project to maximise the benefit while minimising the disbenefits to the environment. For this purpose, we suggest that a good working definition of the environment is

the aggregate of all the external conditions and influences affecting all forms of life on this planet, both now and in the future.

The idealistic concept of sustainability, 'that meets the needs of the present without compromising the ability of future generations to meet their own needs', seems to suggest that sustainability only applies to the human race ('future generations') but we feel sure this is not what was intended by the World Commission. Hence the broad description of the environment in the preceding paragraph. In any case, ideal sustainability cannot be realised while we continue, for example, to use fossil fuels, quarry stone or make steel, cement and bricks.

But we can, and must, work towards the ideal, and everyone approaching the Reviews must demonstrate their awareness of current best practice and how it is implemented in their work. It is unlikely to be sufficient to show that you avoided local waste disposal taxes by keeping potentially hazardous materials within the site, or that you crushed redundant concrete to form aggregate (at what energy cost?).

The Institution has produced guidance on these, and several other, issues; have you read the guidance and put it into practice? If so, tell the Reviewers about it. Candidates for the Chartered Review must additionally demonstrate that they are continually seeking every opportunity to make inroads into further reducing our profligate use of resources.

A commitment to leading sustainable development can be demonstrated by showing that you exploit every opportunity to reduce the use of finite resources, by such everyday means as:

- ensuring fitness for purpose – neither grandiose nor over-demanding over the life cycle
- incorporating reclamation, recycling and re-use
- reducing specifications to allow secondary materials to be used where safety and fitness for purpose are not compromised
- refitting rather than rebuilding
- applying energy conservation measures throughout the whole life cycle.

8. Interpersonal skills and communication

A. The criteria are pretty clear regarding what the Reviewers expect candidates to demonstrate, but it is worth considering how those abilities may be achieved.

B. Engineers must gather, absorb, assess and process information (GAAP) and communicate the result (bridge the GAAP) in a manner which is readily understood by a wide variety of recipients, from operatives to politicians, from pressure groups to colleagues and, most importantly of all, the public, all of whom have differing perspectives and levels of understanding. The continuing suspicion of many of these groups and persistent misunderstandings between colleagues, do suggest that we are not particularly good at achieving this. We have, unfortunately, both heard comments such as, 'They just do not understand what I am talking about!'. That is not the fault of the recipient, but the failure of the communicator to deliver the message in a manner which the recipient can comprehend.

For example,

- How many changes in your work have resulted directly from misunderstandings or lack of information in-house?
- If the general public is overwhelmingly hostile to a proposal, then surely it is our fault; we have not explained the reasoning behind our proposals adequately.
- Any credibility which a pressure group has must be as a result of loopholes in our information supply (or we have made a mistake).

We know that engineers are often confined by political considerations but, in general, we do not believe we take the public into our confidence early enough or sufficiently comprehensively.

Communication is about *information*.

The efficiency of communication is dependent upon the *effective* relaying of *just enough* information to achieve the desired effect on the receiver.

The quality of the information and the method of delivery will determine the level of performance by the receiver.

Information is not just facts, but also covers things such as goals and targets, policy, support, encouragement, discipline, attitudes, even dreams.

C. We now have so many easy, instant methods of communication that we fear that, perversely, they have actually become an obstacle to effective communication. The responsibility for 'separating the wheat from the chaff' has moved from the sender to the receiver, who is deluged with too much information and has to make quick decisions on what to ignore. Inevitably, we are sometimes wrong and fail to recognise important messages. In the context of the Professional Reviews, it is definitely the responsibility of the sender (the candidate) to select the appropriate amount of information to send to the receiver (the Reviewers).

Our Victorian predecessors managed to build mammoth projects all over the world using stagecoaches, sailing ships and slow, overland postal services – because they communicated well. The limited and time-consuming methods available forced them to consider very carefully what needed to be sent to whom, when and how.

Today, all of us suffer from information overload; everyone sends everything to everyone else without any real thought, and seriously believes that they have communicated! Software, email, the internet, project portals and satellite links are only tools; they cannot add to the basic message and unfortunately encourage too much information to be sent to too many people. As a result, we give it all a cursory glance and delete most of it, including, sometimes, key matters which are hidden away in a mass of irrelevant words.

Instant delivery also has the insidious effect of requiring an instant response. The speed of delivery may be instant, but the speed of human thought has not changed for generations. While the sender may expect an instant reply, pause, take time to consider the ramifications of their questions and your possible answers. On more than one occasion an instant response has resulted in a commitment to huge additional, and unbudgeted, expenditure!

Effective communication is achieved by the sender. In Mac's companion book, *Initial Professional Development*, the criteria are listed that result in communication that works. Few people think these important criteria through before firing off a message. If they did, then the internet service providers would certainly notice a significant downturn in traffic. We have heard of some firms' software delaying email replies for 24 hours and disabling the grouping of addresses to force their staff to think about the necessary content and key recipients before responding.

The other contributor to effective communication is the receiver, who must listen (or read). In today's frenetic society, this skill is being lost: the art not only of listening to what the sender is saying, but also of deciphering what they are trying to say. Most people are poor communicators; they send too much information in an unstructured way, hoping the receiver will be able to pick out what they need. Because receivers suffer from information overload and the structure is garbled, the message is lost. You must avoid this at all costs when communicating with your Reviewers. One Reviewer asked his candidate why he had included so many appendices; the answer was, 'I hoped that if I included everything, you could find what you were looking for'! It is your task to *demonstrate*, not the Reviewers' task to find.

During his seminars, Mac experimented with the TV weather forecast, recording it beforehand and then asking delegates what the weather was going to be in their area immediately after the presenter had finished. He was amazed by the answers he was given, and the resulting embarrassment when he replayed the forecast and, for the first time, the delegates actually listened. The sophisticated graphics available, the apparent need for an animated personality, the desire to justify their predictions by showing what is going on out in the Atlantic, all actually obscure the presenter's message. The weather forecast has perhaps become entertainment rather than clear, precise information. Indeed, much of modern media communication is about superficial sound bites, often unsubstantiated. Beware of doing something similar, particularly in your Review documents, presentation and interview.

You will, almost inevitably, find it difficult to convey to your Reviewers 'just enough' information. The temptation will be to tell them everything, in the hope that they can pick out what is relevant. Most of you will, in our experience, start with a report which is far too long, and have to edit it significantly to come within the word count. In Chapter 10 on the Professional Review Report we suggest ways in which you can avoid this chore. Remember – you must *demonstrate* your capabilities; the Reviewers are not required to seek them out. One of those abilities is to convey important messages clearly and succinctly.

You may perhaps believe that integrated management system procedures help to ensure good communication by quality assurance. In our experience, quality assurance is a control system for the *process* of relaying information, providing an audit trail of what was done and said, by whom, and why. But it does not control or measure the *efficiency* of communication: only that it happened. Few systems measure outcomes.

D. The concept of embracing diversity aims to recognise, respect and value people's differences, encouraging them to contribute and realise their full potential by promoting an inclusive culture for all people within and outside your place of employment. Every organisation in the European Union is required to have a statement of its principles and practice. You will be expected to know what your employer's statement says and to have views on its problems, effectiveness and possible modification. Where you are involved in projects in different cultures, you will be expected to have learnt and understood any differences in approach compared to your home jurisdiction. Most of us now work regularly with persons of differing backgrounds and it is vital that we understand any differences in outlook or behaviour if we are to communicate effectively without misunderstandings. Describe situations where you have done this.

The whole issue of diversity cannot be separated from equality. Equality is managing diversity issues to ensure that individuals or groups of individuals are treated fairly and equally and that none is treated less favourably, including on the grounds of race, gender, disability, religion or beliefs, sexual orientation and age. This treatment must be specific to their personal needs and abilities, so it does not mean that everyone should be equal, but that they must have equal access to suitable opportunities to enable them to fully participate in the workload, thus enabling all staff and ancillary workers to develop to their full potential.

Confronting diversity issues should remove discrimination in all of the areas mentioned in the above paragraph; this includes bullying, harassment or victimisation. None of these has been entirely eradicated from the workplace so far, but all are now being taken much more seriously.

9. Professional commitment

Too often, this Attribute has been narrowly interpreted as accumulating sufficient Continuing Professional Development (CPD) days and attending the odd 'civils' or professional meeting. In our view, it means far more than that. It is, to paraphrase the Institution,

> the exercise of professional skill and judgement with integrity and to the best of our ability to safeguard the public interest in matters of safety, public health and the environment and to uphold the dignity and reputation of our profession.

Professional commitment is about ethics, responsibility and morals. You will inadvertently reveal your true attitudes during the Review as you answer questions and express opinions. So do make sure you have read, understand and have put into practice the Institution's guidance on ethics and conduct, so that it has become an intrinsic part of your attitude to life and work.

It is almost certain that your Reviewers will want to learn how much of the Institution's code of conduct you know and particularly how this may be relevant in your professional life.

Summary

All these Review criteria enlarge on the Institution's Royal Charter, which all candidates profess to have read and understood prior to applying for the Review:

a profession which calls for a high degree of professional knowledge and
judgement in
  making the best use of scarce resources
  care for the environment and
  the interests of public health and safety.

The key word implicit throughout all these descriptions is judgement. It will not be
enough to demonstrate that you always comply with 'the rules'. The rules must inevitably
be out of date, based as they are on previous experience, and there will be occasions when
they cannot be applied sensibly. That is when your judgement comes into play. A senior
lawyer once offered a fundamental explanation of the basic thought process we go
through for every decision:

At this time, with these resources, in these circumstances, for the foreseeable
future, this, in my considered opinion, is the best solution.

Having made that judgement, the decision can be defended as correct in a court of law.
This does not mean that this particular solution is absolute, correct for all time, since any
of those factors can, and probably will, change in the future.

Successful Professional Reviews for Civil Engineers
ISBN 978-0-7277-6100-2

ICE Publishing: All rights reserved
http://dx.doi.org/10.1680/sprce61002.045

ice
Institution of Civil Engineers

publishing

Chapter 7
Difference between a Member (or Associate) and a Chartered Member

There is a clear distinction between the attributes of a Chartered Member and those of a Member or Associate. This was clearly spelt out by the Council of the Institution in 1998:

> A Member (or Associate) is an expert in their particular field. Their role demands a practical approach, considerable technical (or scientific) competence and some managerial expertise and control in a particular aspect of the construction industry, with an understanding of the whole procurement process and an appreciation of the social, economic and environmental impact of their involvement.

> A Chartered Member, on the other hand, combines a thorough understanding of technical principles with broad, multi-disciplinary professional and leadership capability to enable them to effectively and safely direct, change and progress the infrastructure and built environment by balancing financial, social, environmental and political implications and the effective and beneficial management of resources.

Generally, engineers do seem to divide into different kinds of people. Some are at their best 'doing' the technical engineering; they consider that persuading politicians and a sceptical public of the legitimacy of their proposals or seeking permissions and managing resources is frustrating, or they may not, so far, have had the opportunities to operate at these interfaces. Others revel in the challenge and conflict of trying to convince the public that what is being proposed is the best compromise solution, or of working in and organising a multi-disciplinary environment, but always retaining sufficient technical understanding to realise the full implications of what they and their associates are doing.

At the Member Professional Review, you must exhibit a high standard of expertise in a limited range of work, where you could, if necessary, supervise others doing similar tasks. But you are also expected to understand the whole context of your work. So, dependent on your particular area of expertise, your profile might look something like this:

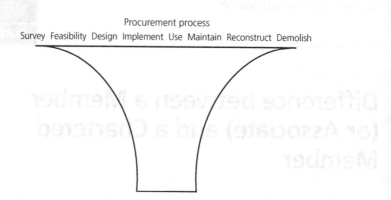

Procurement process
Survey Feasibility Design Implement Use Maintain Reconstruct Demolish

You are very competent in your role, know and understand how it relates to those working close to you and have some idea of how your work fits into the entire process. The area of greatest expertise will clearly swing from one extreme to the other. Someone working in feasibility surveys, for example, will swing well to the start of the procurement process; someone in demolition will swing to the right, the end of the process.

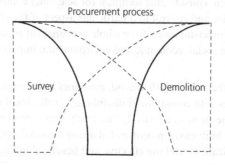

Procurement process

Survey   Demolition

As a candidate for Chartered Membership, you are expected to have developed a greater depth of understanding of the whole procurement process, gained partly by reading widely and partly by experience. So you may not perhaps have quite such a depth of expertise in any particular specialisation; your profile might look something like this:

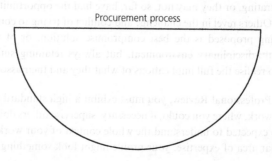

Procurement process

For completeness, the profile of a Technician Member is even more pronounced, where they know a great deal about one particular aspect of the procurement process, and relatively little about the whole process, apart from how they interface with their immediate colleagues.

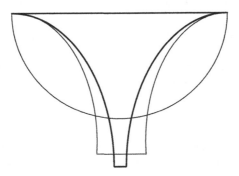

Obviously these profiles are a gross over-simplification of reality. They do in a sense divide the world into racehorses and Shire horses – both good at their job but capable of doing the other job, though perhaps not particularly well (although we quite fancy the idea of a Shire horse race). Where do eventers, steeplechasers or hurdlers fit in? Somewhere in the envelopes below? Even more difficult to place is the highly developed dressage horse.

Your personal profile, when you completed your academic education, probably looked more like that of the Incorporated Member, but has broadened out since as you gained experience. At the time of the Review, it probably veers like a jagged saw from one side of the envelopes to the other, dependent on your particular experiences, neither truly one nor the other:

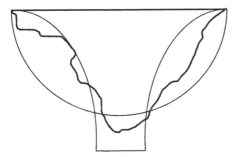

What is vital is that you tailor your preparation and submission to suit the profile you have chosen to demonstrate. The differences are not quite as straightforward as these cartoon profiles suggest, but the figures do give an indication of the fundamental manner in which apparently similar attributes are assessed by the Reviewers, dependent upon which Review is being attempted.

When last revising the routes to membership, the Institution anticipated that the majority would gain early professional qualification through the Member Professional Review (MPR). Once opportunities became available, some would broaden out to exert a significant influence beyond a strictly engineering or technical context and become Chartered Members through the progressive route. There are a few who innately have the qualities in their psyche, and can become Chartered Engineers very quickly. But the majority still seek Chartered Membership as the first step and, unfortunately, the results indicate that too many are falling short. If they applied for MPR, many more should qualify as MICE earlier.

The timing of these opportunities will depend to a considerable extent on the expectations and needs of your employer and on your developing capabilities as an individual. Some engineers will have been recruited specifically to fast-track into roles represented by the criteria for CEng; others will gradually move into those roles, while some will prefer to become experts in a technological field. One route is not better than the other, just different. One problem seems to be that some organisations' salary scales still do not accept these differences or recognise the value of having a mix of skilled individuals forming a suitably effective team.

Not until you are personally satisfied that you fully comply with one of the descriptions outlined in Appendix A should you proceed any further.

Until you honestly believe that you *are* a professional of the appropriate grade, do not apply!

We cannot see how you can possibly convince others of your capabilities unless you truly believe yourself to be capable. The preparation, drafting and collation of a submission is a long and laborious process, not to be undertaken lightly and surely not without a reasonable chance of success? Seek the guidance of wise colleagues whose opinions you can trust. The idea that you should make an application merely because you are 'time-served' or seeking a promotion that is dependent on gaining a professional qualification must not be allowed to cloud your judgement. An unsuccessful attempt is a waste of time and resources and a hugely disappointing blow to your self-esteem.

Successful Professional Reviews for Civil Engineers
ISBN 978-0-7277-6100-2

ICE Publishing: All rights reserved
http://dx.doi.org/10.1680/sprce61002.049

Chapter 8
Starting the submission

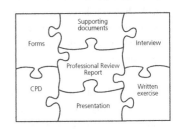

Once you have decided that you are a professional engineer, capable of becoming an Institution Member, the next question you need to ask yourself is:

How am I going to demonstrate my competence?

From this point on, everything you do, everything you write, every form you complete, all the supporting documents you collect, are all aimed at one specific target – proving that you are a professional engineer of the appropriate grade. You must ensure that your jigsaw picture is complete, with each piece locked into the others and with no gaps or overlaps anywhere.

One of the things which ought to have intrigued potential candidates is:

Why does it appear to be so complicated?

Why, for example, can you not just submit an expanded CV and attend an interview? The answer is that, having interviewed candidates since 1897 and after some 70 years' experience of the Review in a format recognisable today, the Institution thinks that this is the best format (so far) for candidates to be able to effectively demonstrate their full abilities. In other words, the format has been refined through long experience to give you the best possible chance of demonstrating your capability as a professional.

So every part matters and must be of use to the Reviewers; what you have to do is find out what the Reviewers need from each part and then make sure you fulfil their expectations.

The first, and perhaps rather obvious, point about your preparation is:

Make sure you comply with the current rules.

It is surprising just how many candidates do not. It does not automatically mean that they will fail, but it certainly does put them at an immediate disadvantage.

49

You need to make sure that your copy of the specification or rules is the most recent version. Once you have made the decision to proceed, go to the Institution's website and download the latest guidance. If necessary, contact the Institution's local staff to check that you have the right documents for the Review you intend to take. After all, you would not commence a civil engineering contract without the latest set of documents and standards, would you? And yet we have come across candidates whose preparation of their submission has been based almost entirely upon hearsay!

Then spend some time reading the documents thoroughly. It never ceases to surprise us just how many candidates reveal during a discussion that they are unfamiliar with detailed points in the ICE publications. It pays to make notes or annotate the document to make sure you are entirely clear which parts relate to you and which are irrelevant (you could do the same with the guidance in this book – but in pencil, in case someone else wishes to use it). And then we suggest you read *and digest* the parts you have highlighted as relevant, to be absolutely certain that you fully understand what is required. If in doubt, make use of the ICE Regional Support Team.

Only when you are absolutely clear on how to set about the submission (and, of course, that you are prepared for Review) should you start. One important part of the submission, which is usually left until too late, is the administration – the forms.

The requirements for the initial application

The Institution has set out its requirements for the initial application in its publication, *Professional Review Guidance*. You are required to specify the centre (location) where you want to sit your Review – the dates and locations are shown on the Institution website. If you are tempted to choose the venue which is last chronologically in the hope of gaining a little more time to put the submission together, then this would strongly suggest that you are not properly ready to undertake the Review.

Your initial application has to be submitted as a single PDF file of no more than 5MB in size. The appearance of your application matters and you should therefore arrange to have access to good quality PDF-writing software, rather than relying on free plug-ins or, worse still, scanning hard-copy documents into PDF format. If necessary, you can seek help from a suitable copy shop or other printing business. The Institution does not specify file name notation but we think that you should follow the advice given for the subsequent submission of your report and use the following format:

member number_name_review date_document type
12345678_B.BREMNER_11.10.15_APPLICATION

You must email your file to the Institution by the applicable deadline, which will be shown on the website along with the Review dates.

Your initial application should include:

- the application form
- the Review fee
- sponsor questionnaires, submitted separately by your sponsors
- evidence that you have the required qualifications, unless these have already been approved
- evidence of Initial Professional Development (IPD) completion
- your CV
- a one-page précis of your Professional Review Report
- evidence of any special requirements you need taken into account (e.g. security/ vetting – where the subject matter of your submission may only be considered by Reviewers with the necessary clearance, such as military, security or criminal justice projects – or accessibility).

The application form

A key component of the submission is the various application documents . These too are, perhaps unexpectedly, a crucial part of the jigsaw. It is amazing just how many candidates fill them in incorrectly. They seem to be left to the last minute and are completed hurriedly, without any thought being given to why all this information is needed. We presume this is because they are not seen as a particularly important part of the submission, yet they can help significantly with the overall impression.

The initial application *will* create an impression and will be the first indication of you that your Reviewers see when they access the Reviews' online portal. Like all the other pieces, this piece of the jigsaw must be used to support your claim to be a professional engineer. The application form can be completed on computer or by hand but we strongly recommend the former. Untidy or difficult to read submissions, boxes poorly filled in with an inappropriate pencil (even if the information itself is correct): all conspire to make people wonder; to raise initial doubts about your professional capabilities. And certainly do not leave this task to the last minute and hurriedly complete it, only to have your submission returned as non-compliant.

Table A on the application form asks you to state your area of technical expertise by ticking one of a series of options. This grid matches that completed by the Reviewers, where they indicate to the Institution what they feel capable of examining. This is the way the computer selection process ensures that at least one of your Reviewers is reasonably familiar with your sphere of work. So tick the boxes that best indicate the areas with which you would like one of your Reviewers to be familiar.

Table B asks you to indicate your type of employment. The categories are wide and you may feel that you do not exactly fit any of them. It does not matter too much; just choose the one which most closely indicates your employment. This is just another device to help the computer and Institution staff to choose suitable Reviewers.

Review fee

The fees and the methods of payment are shown on the Institution website and you should pay careful attention to getting these right. Applications received without payment of the appropriate fee are usually disregarded by the ICE.

Payment of the fee is made online, except by special arrangement, so it is hard to see how you can include payment with your initial application. We assume therefore that the Institution expects you to include proof of payment, so ensure that you keep the receipt and confirmation issued by the ICE website once you have paid. Occasionally technical problems affect web payment systems so you should pay for your Review a few days before applying to ensure that you have received proof of payment by the time you submit your initial application.

Sponsor questionnaires

Your sponsors should be chosen with care, not just a collection of available people from your office. They do have to answer some quite searching questions which you should read before asking people to commit themselves. It does no favours for candidates when the Institution is told, 'I am not in a position to answer this question' or 'Others may be better able to answer this question'. If someone you have chosen expresses doubts or uncertainty, find out why. It may only be because they feel they are not up to date with current standards, but it could be that they are not sure of your chances of success. In which case, you need to sit down and discuss it with them – they may, after all, have a point! A candidate who was unsuccessful once came back to Mac after he had refused to sponsor him and said, 'You were the only one who was honest. Will you help me with a resit?'. Mac did.

Patrick once reviewed a candidate whose group of sponsors did not include anyone from his employing organisation, which is very rare, almost unique. One of his sponsors, a chartered civil engineer, happened to be a neighbour of the candidate's parents but knew nothing of the career now under consideration. His reference was worthless in the context of the Review.

If you trained under agreement, one sponsor should normally be the person who trained you – your SCE; but if that Agreement ended some time ago and you lost touch with them shortly after they registered your Completion Certificate, are they in the best position to vouch for you now *as a professional engineer*? You may need to update them on what you have done since you were in close contact, perhaps by giving them a copy of your draft reports and visiting them for a discussion.

While not a requirement, we think it appropriate to ask your sponsors to indicate those parts of your experience of which they have direct knowledge – first, it authenticates that experience and, second, it demonstrates that they have seen and read your report and should have decided whether they think you have a reasonable chance of success – something your Lead Sponsor is required to have done.

Do not necessarily look for sponsors solely within your own organisation. Why not ask someone from your project's consultant/contractor/client/promoter to signify their respect for you as a professional engineer? While you may have had contractual differences and disagreements, surely the Reviewers will be favourably impressed by their opinion of you as a professional? Think about the impression you are making all the time – the *purpose* – and choose your sponsors accordingly.

There is no room on the form for additional sponsors, so it is vital that you choose the best available to you within the criteria set down by the ICE. This requires that your Lead Sponsor must be a Member of at least the same grade as that for which you are submitting. The rest need not necessarily be Members, but must be members of other Institutions governed by the Engineering Council or with whom the ICE has a mutual agreement on qualification.

The Lead Sponsor

You have to nominate one of your sponsors as the Lead Sponsor; you may wonder why. The reason is that the Institution has become irritated by people sponsoring candidates who are totally unsuitable (often without even seeing the submission documents) and wishes to be able to reprimand those who do. This situation can result from an inaccurate or outdated perception of what the Institution requires of candidates; by putting the onus very much on the Lead Sponsor, the Institution expects them to familiarise themselves with the current requirements.

The Institution offers the following guidance to sponsors in their questionnaire:

> In the event that the Reviewers consider a candidate's performance varies significantly from that described by the Sponsor or expected by ICE at Review, feedback to the Lead Sponsor will occur. It is expected that the Lead Sponsor will consider such feedback as part of a learning review.

Your Lead Sponsor therefore has serious professional responsibilities. To be properly accountable to the Institution for their opinion of you, they must be a Member of an appropriate grade. Their responsibilities are threefold:

(*a*) to satisfy themselves that you have a realistic chance of proving you have become a professional engineer (*b*) to certify that your submission is a reasonable and honest reflection of your experience and capabilities

(*c*) to check that none of your other sponsors has misgivings either.

So do not put them in an uncomfortable position; give them everything they need to wholeheartedly support your application.

Getting the report ready for your Lead Sponsor

One implication behind the responsibilities outlined above is that, before your sponsors (and particularly your Lead Sponsor) can complete their forms, you must have your submission documents pretty well finalised. Bearing in mind the logistics of asking them if they are prepared to sponsor you, sending out the forms, completion, and return to the Lead Sponsor, who may email or post the form directly to the Institution, the date for completion of this aspect should be about one month before submission.

Don't delay! We despair of the number of candidates who apply to sit their Review in the centre chronologically last in the list to give themselves another month for preparation; it is mistaken and foolhardy, as technology is enabling the Institution to tighten up the whole process, thereby reducing waiting times. It is hardly surprising that the names of such candidates tend to appear in the 'unsuccessful' results list.

If you kept a number of photographs and other material, such as calculations and brochures, with your records during training, go through them in detail to see whether or which of them will help the Reviewers – remembering the overriding objective. If they are more of an aid to your own recall, then remove them.

Evidence that you have the required qualifications

In most cases this will have been demonstrated where candidates are already graduate members of the Institution. Where you still have to demonstrate that your qualifications are compliant, ensure that you seek guidance from the Institution in advance to establish what is required.

Evidence of IPD completion

This must be one of the following three documents:

■   ICE Completion Certificate
■   ICE Career Appraisal letter
■   other appropriate documents from Hong Kong Institution of Engineers.

The procedures involved in obtaining these documents fall outside of the remit of this book. Our only advice is to allow sufficient time for completing the necessary formalities of these processes as part of your build-up to your Review.

A CV suitable for professional qualification purposes

The CV needed here is to assist the Institution staff and your Reviewers to understand your current and past roles. There is further guidance on the Institution website about what to include.

Please note that the purpose of this CV is very different from the other occasions where you may be asked for one, such as when applying for a new job or being proposed for a role by your employer. In the Institution's own words:

ICE will be seeking to verify, from the information contained in your CV, how you have achieved the required levels of competence in [each of] the attribute areas.

Therefore your CV submitted here needs to show how this was done.

One-page précis

As a manual check on the process of matching candidates to appropriate Reviewers, you are also asked to submit 'a précis of the significant work section of your proposed report'. This is neither a synopsis nor a summary, so make sure you understand what you are trying to do. We would strongly suggest that it should never exceed one A4 page and in many cases should be only one or two sentences.

synopsis: condensed statement, often with headings and sub-headings, retaining the general sense and unity of the work or treatise

summary: brief, concise but comprehensive statement; the removal of all that is superfluous

précis: brief summary of the main principles of the content of a larger work
(definitions compiled from a variety of dictionary sources)

To decide what are the main principles which should be summarised, you need to know why a précis is required. It is the means by which the Reviewers can check that at least one of the chosen pair is sufficiently familiar with your work to be able to comprehend the principles. You need to indicate in broad terms the kind of work that the Professional Review Report covers and the sector of the business from which you have gained the best experience.

So the précis may only be a short paragraph, if that is all that is needed to give an indication of the type of work covered. It could be as simple as:

My six years' experience is in a consultancy specialising in the design of wastewater treatment works, with a year on the site supervision of construction of a third-stage treatment plant. My Report explains my role in the feasibility studies for a plant in Hampshire treating raw sewage to produce effluent which meets river discharge consents, with detailed design of a settlement tank.

Again, once you know the purpose, the requirements become more obvious. We have heard of people taking hours to write a comprehensive synopsis because they mistakenly presumed it was similar to that needed for a thesis.

Evidence of any special requirements
The Institution suggests that the special requirements may include elements of accessibility or disability and restrictions on security. If you have any special requirements then you are required to provide evidence of these, for example a medical certificate or a letter from your doctor.

Successful Professional Reviews for Civil Engineers
ISBN 978-0-7277-6100-2

Chapter 9
Continuing Professional Development

Continuing Professional Development (CPD) is defined by the Institution as:

> the systematic maintenance, improvement and broadening of knowledge and
> skills, and the development of personal qualities necessary for the execution of
> professional and technical duties throughout your working life.

It is obligatory; Rule 5 of the Institution's Rules of Professional Conduct states:

> All members shall develop their professional knowledge, skills and competence on
> a continuing basis and shall give all reasonable assistance to further the
> education, training and continuing professional development of others.

Currently, the Council's recommendation is that every qualified Member records enough
hours of CPD:

> to develop and maintain the professional knowledge, skills and competence that
> you need.

However, the Institution still requires those submitting for a Professional Review to
demonstrate a minimum CPD commitment of 30 hours of effective learning per year
for a minimum of three years.

A day's training is taken to be six hours of useful personal development, however long the
day actually was. You cannot count anything done for another purpose (such as an MSc
used to top up your academic base) towards your total. This requirement is in accord with
nearly all the professional Institutions and is likely to increase in time. The Institution
now routinely monitors, on a random sample basis, the CPD records of those on its
various panels, for example adjudicators, arbitrators and the Reviewers who will
conduct your Professional Review.

Do take due note of this obligation to average 30 hours per year. If your total experience
(including vacations or sandwich course time) extends beyond a period of three (MPR) or
six (CPR) years (and many candidates' experience does) then this requirement takes

precedence and the stated minimum of 90 (MPR) or 180 (CPR) hours becomes inadequate.

Your recording of your CPD is vital and the Institution has an online CPD tool which is accessible from your 'MyICE' page. It is not obligatory that you use this, however, and the traditional paper forms are equally acceptable. Some ICE Members are also members of other professional institutions and there is no requirement for you to duplicate your records.

The ICE's recommended approach to CPD is the CPD cycle – see below – which includes the four stages of reviewing, planning, developing and assessing your CPD. The ICE recommends the use of a Development Action Plan (DAP) and Personal Development Record (PDR) to do this and has templates available for your use. However, as long as your records identify these four stages then they will be accepted by the Institution.

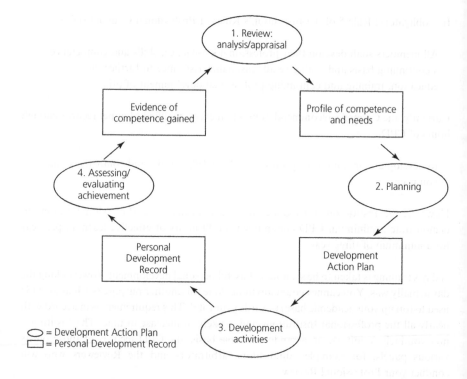

CPD – why bother?

The requirement is sometimes viewed by employers with alarm, particularly in terms of the cost implications of 'sending everyone on courses' – not merely the cost of the course, but the productive time lost and expenses involved. Most employers have now realised that this is a mistaken overreaction. In effect, everything you now know, which you did not know when you graduated, must, by definition, be *continuing* professional development. Many employers have developed HR management systems which include the facility to allow you to benefit from an adequately documented quality assurance system. We have both noticed the link between the calibre of the engineers we meet on our training courses and the respective employers' commitment to CPD for their staff.

Routinely, evidence of CPD is required when you join; when you change level of Membership, notably from Member to Fellow; if you apply to be an SCE or Reviewer; and for certain professional functions, such as adjudication, arbitration and reservoir inspection. In addition, the ICE is monitoring a small, random percentage of Members' records every year. This has become a realistic option as the majority of us record our CPD online.

Perhaps more significantly, think about the possible implications if you:

(*a*) give evidence in a legal/contractual case
(*b*) need Professional Indemnity insurance
(*c*) are accused of professional negligence (a possibility perhaps more likely than hitherto, given today's litigious attitudes)
(*d*) are required by a client to disclose the qualifications of all staff you intend to use on a project as part of a tender proposal.

Would it not be reasonable for the lawyers, insurers or client to ask what you have done to maintain or enhance your professional competence since qualification? How would your firm react if they were asked, point blank, 'What right has this employee to be making such decisions?' and they were unable to *prove* (to the satisfaction of the risk assessor) your up-to-date knowledge and competence. The response 'He has a degree in civil engineering gained six years ago' is not going to be adequate. Record what you are doing to keep yourself reasonably up to date and improve your competence and neither you nor your employer will be caught out.

What does CPD entail?

Since a CPD record became a requirement, engineers have found that they are, in fact, already doing at least the minimum and, in most cases, considerably more. Today's rapid changes, not only in technology and the legal framework, but also constant reorganisation and redeployment, mean that anyone who does not keep their knowledge up to date or learn new skills will soon be left far behind. Flexibility and adaptability are vital commodities in today's uncertain market-place; for these, CPD is a prerequisite.

The list published by the Institution in its CPD guidance covers all the methods of keeping up to date; they go far beyond 'going on courses'. It is possible to fulfil the minimum requirement without ever attending a course, although there are some things which are best covered in a structured environment. The only proviso is that, since the system is self-certifying, it is preferable for there to be some tangible end result, to use as proof for audit if ever needed.

In practice, therefore, the requirement is not an additional imposition, simply that you properly record what is probably already being done.

What CPD is needed?

CPD is a method of continual self-development; it should be an intrinsic part of your continuing training and development, not a 'bolt-on' extra. It is necessary to routinely examine your current levels of skills and knowledge and measure these against those that already are, or probably will be required in the future. This is not difficult if approached in a rational and formal way. Many organisations now have formal systems for annual assessment of their staff and their training needs but, if yours does not, do it yourself in the Institution's Development Action Plan. You then need to record what you actually did to make good any identified deficiency in your Professional Development Record.

If your employer already has a documented system in place for routinely (perhaps annually) assessing the effectiveness of last year's CPD and planning next year's, and is willing to allow it to be used by you for the Review, then don't waste time duplicating information. Get permission to photocopy their record. But beware, some companies only record formal CPD, such as courses and seminars, partly because they are entitled to seek reimbursement of these expenses from industry and Government funding bodies. Such a record will only show a small part of the total effort you are putting into keeping up to date and developing.

The key criteria for professional development are:

continuing, relevant and progressive.

Going on a basic site safety course three years after first working on site is a prerequisite – merely 'complying with the rules', neither progressive nor relevant. While it will not be a reason for failure, it could well be held in evidence against you.

A strong indicator of relevance for one critical aspect is supplied by the Attributes. How are you going to develop the required competences? Some things are best learnt by 'hands-on' experience; others are best learnt about on courses and then put into practice. We expect most candidates to have had formal training in the fundamentally important matters of hazard and risk identification and management, and probably the commercial context of their work. These, and similar topics, are too important to be learnt solely by experience – they could be expensive lessons!

Also, look carefully at the personal qualities being developed, which are necessary to many other professions: things such as time management, team working, personal relationships, negotiating skills, running a small business, a second language. You do not necessarily need a civil engineering course to learn the basics of these. Consider material and courses beyond civil engineering – the local Chamber of Commerce, Further and Higher Educational courses (both vocational and recreational) and distance learning material from other Institutions.

What the Reviewers will be looking for is a concerted and considered programme to put right areas of your expertise which you have identified as needing attention. If you find using the English language difficult (and many engineers do) then have you tried to improve by attendance on a suitable course? If you have had difficulty with contractual disagreements or public meetings, have you been on a course to develop negotiating skills or to help in dealing with the public? If you went to work in a laboratory, did you first find out what the hazards were likely to be and how to avoid them?

Most employers put new employees through an induction process, to explain the workplace and what is expected of them. This is, of course, by definition, professional development – have you recorded the lessons you learnt about the way the business is organised and your responsibilities as an employee?

Do keep in mind the Council's current recommendation – an average of 30 hours per year for CPR. The minimum requirement for the Review (indeed, for the Training Review or Career Appraisal) may not be applicable if it has taken rather longer to reach that key stage in your professional development. Again, of itself, this would not be a reason for failure, but it is going to raise doubts about your commitment.

CPD is another important part of the total jigsaw, not an appendage! It is part of your overall development and will be consistent with your Reports.

Successful Professional Reviews for Civil Engineers
ISBN 978-0-7277-6100-2

ICE Publishing: All rights reserved
http://dx.doi.org/10.1680/sprce61002.063

Chapter 10
The Professional Review Report

The Professional Review Report (the 'Report') is the key vehicle for you to demonstrate that you have achieved the Attributes. The Report is to enable you to demonstrate that, as a result of your experience, you have developed and have used, or could use, all the capabilities needed by a qualified Member of the Institution of the grade for which you are applying.

You can utilise anything which enables you to display your competence. The content might be your entire job, or bits of various recent work or one extensive project. This decision on what to include needs careful thought, always bearing in mind that the aim is to display that you have developed and, wherever possible, utilised every one of the required capabilities. It requires a careful balance between the various work which needs to be described and the need to clearly identify the qualities displayed or developed by you; the more work needing description, the fewer words there are for your 'demonstration of competence'. This is where careful compilation of your specific CV at the same time can be of great help.

The rules say that you should have had a major involvement and some degree of responsibility, such that you are able to demonstrate the required capabilities. In other words, the Report must *demonstrate* either that you have, or that you could (given the chance) readily and confidently take on the responsibilities and display all the attributes of a qualified Member.

This is an interesting and difficult concept for those well-schooled in scholastic examinations, where the emphasis seems very much on the transmission of as much knowledge as possible or on 'getting the correct answer'. Few academic examinations measure potential; most retrospectively measure what you have learnt and can put into practice. At the Review, there is an element of potential capability upon which the Reviewers must make a judgement. You are attempting to answer the question:

> Would this candidate, when placed in a position of responsibility, make the correct decisions?

Note that the wording is 'Would', not 'Has'. As we said in Chapter 4, you are not yet a qualified Member, so may not yet be allowed to take decisions commensurate with the status you are seeking. But you must demonstrate that you could! You should know enough about the background of decisions being taken on the work, by those senior to you, to be capable of making similar decisions in future.

So start from the qualities of a Member qualified at your target grade; how can each be demonstrated through the intended work? Use your training record and other accumulated documentation to provide inspiration and information. Make notes! It is surprising how readily ideas can be lost if they are not recorded at the time you think of them. This detailed stage will take time, so don't leave it to the last minute. Indeed, you ought perhaps to have done the exercise in essence before you committed to the Review.

This Report need not be on one project – it can be based on several from your most recent experience. It could even be on your entire role (for example, 'providing specialist geotechnical advice to a major consultancy – with particular reference to... projects').

But be careful in your choice. Remember, you are going to demonstrate *your* abilities and the more words used to describe the work, the fewer remain for this prime purpose. Work backwards from what the Reviewers are seeking to identify; which of your project roles would enable you to best demonstrate those capabilities? Use an abbreviated list of the keywords from the Attributes. You will probably find that the most useful experience was also your most rewarding; not necessarily the neatest or most complete, but the one where you battled successfully through a number of complex problems. This 'back to front' approach avoids the process of writing far too much and then having to edit it down to fit the specified word count.

You will probably write the greater proportion of your Report on your most recent experience. We believe you that should for three reasons:

(*a*) You are probably a better engineer today than yesterday – 'old' experience is therefore less likely to demonstrate your full abilities.
(*b*) You are likely to be more familiar with current work and, therefore, better able to discuss it in detail at interview.
(*c*) Documentary 'evidence' is probably easier to assemble, since it is likely to be on your desk.

The work need not be particularly large or 'grand'; the overriding requirement is that it must enable demonstration of your capabilities as a potential qualified Member – technical or managerial complexity are more important than prestige.

Most engineers tend to take what they do for granted; they are essentially problem solvers. Once a problem is overcome, they move on to the next one and the original problem slips into their subconscious; only the solution is remembered. It is therefore difficult to recall everything of relevance. Hence, the importance of good diaries and training records and the need for time to unravel the original problem from your records and memory.

Once you have completed making notes on the individual Attributes, as outlined in Chapter 6, you will have at least sufficient material for this part of your Report. The next stage is to organise the information into a coherent whole. Your notes comprise a list of ingredients. It is unlikely that the pudding (the Report) will look at all like the ingredients, but the Reviewers should be able to detect all of them as they read the Report, just as they might taste the individual ingredients in a pudding. Tackling it this way will ensure that you write mostly about your role, responsibilities, understanding and experience and a minimum about the project(s), and thus avoid a lot of time-consuming editing.

Complying with the Institution's requirements

The Institution has set out its requirements for the Report in its publication, *Professional Review Guidance*. Rather than repeating the requirements verbatim here, we have broken them down into a series of bullet points and we offer advice as to how candidates should comply with each. The requirements are:

- up to 5000 words long
- your own work
- presented in an orderly manner
- emphasise your responsibilities and experience for each Attribute
- expand on decisions you made, problems you encountered, occasions when you gained unusual or extensive experience and learnt valuable lessons
- include a description of a particular project, or projects
- describe how you took a lead in some or all of the elements (CPR only)
- clearly indicate your role in any relevant aspects of the projects, giving background to important decisions you were responsible for or made a significant contribution to
- show where you exercised independent judgement
- a brief, two-page CV
- Appendices (we shall look at these later in Chapter 12).

Up to 5000 words long

You have 5000 words to allocate to the Report and this may initially appear to be generous. However, our experience of working with candidates is that this limit will be reached well before the Report is finished. As with all areas of the Review you must plan how to utilise this limit and how the Report coordinates with the other elements of the Review, particularly the presentation. It is likely that your more recent experience will be effective in satisfying the Attributes and you should therefore allocate words accordingly. Note that candidates pursuing the CPRP have a limit of 2000 words.

To further minimise the 'waste' of words on explaining the project, make judicious use of sketches, maps and plans or photographs, each one chosen with care to illustrate exactly what you need. If figures (traffic counts, flows, areas, etc.) would be useful for the Reviewers to better appreciate the scale of the work, then annotate the sketch or plan as appropriate. By doing this, you retain as many words as possible to demonstrate your influence on the progress of the work.

Too many candidates sprinkle photographs liberally around their Reports, without any clear purpose beyond the vain hope that they might impress the Reviewers. Beware! Pictures of the job, however prestigious, will certainly not impress and may even inadvertently give the Reviewers the opportunity to raise an awkward query about some detail in the image.

The ideal is to refer to a definitive picture, perhaps annotated with key facts about the work (possibly on the front cover), then briefly and succinctly describe the project and the background to it in the first half (no more than two-thirds) of a page, so that you can start on your role within the first 100 words or so. This is not always possible, but it is a target.

We have seen a Report where the cover had a picture of a mapped grey shape of an urban centre with arrows indicating the rush hour flows in and out on all the major arteries and a very big number in the middle – the total number of vehicles in one day! The candidate's Report started, 'I was to ensure the smooth flow of vehicles in the urban centre'. No more – ideal!

Much more about the supporting documentation is included in Chapter 12.

Your own work
The preparation of the Report is 'open book' and you are perfectly entitled to seek assistance from others. Indeed, your Reviewers are likely to be unforgiving of any errors in presentation, spelling, grammar, consistency, etc. Therefore you should seek the counsel of others. Remember though, that this Report is about *you* and will be used by the Reviewers to assess *your* application. So make sure that the Report is your work, notwithstanding the support that you are legitimately entitled to receive from others, whether friends, colleagues or family.

Presented in an orderly manner
It is essential that you consider your audience at all stages in the Review process. Your two Reviewers will be qualified civil engineers and are therefore (like most professional engineers) likely to be logical thinkers. That is usually one outcome of an engineering education. There are no set rules as to how you structure your Report but you must ensure that you set it out logically. There is a story to follow and it should be immediately apparent to the Reviewers how you have demonstrated the Attributes.

Emphasise your responsibilities and experience for each Attribute

This is a task that many engineers find difficult. Explaining 'what we do' can be daunting and many professional engineers undersell themselves or fail to explain the full extent of their responsibilities. Job titles vary from one place to another, so it is insufficient to say that you were a project manager or a principal engineer. Candidates must ensure that both words, responsibilities *and* experience, are addressed. Your responsibilities will have been allocated to you by your employer; your experience is what happened to you while managing those responsibilities. The Institution requires that you address each Attribute, so ensure that all nine headings have been explained.

Expand on decisions you made, problems you encountered, occasions when you gained unusual or extensive experience and learnt valuable lessons

This requirement is central to demonstrating your case. Anyone who claims not to have encountered these four things in their career has not been paying sufficient attention. These four elements all provide opportunities for you to explain what you did and thereby satisfy aspects of the Attributes.

Include a description of a particular project, or projects

Candidates need to describe their project(s) to allow the Reviewers to place the experience claimed into context. Remember that your Reviewers will not be familiar with your work.

> For example, 'A1 upgrade' tells the audience little. Instead, '£380 M upgrade of 19 km of dual carriageway to motorway standard' provides much more context. You can save words by careful drafting of the two-page CV (dealt with below).

Describe how you took a lead in some or all of the elements (CPR only)

Leadership is a key component of the CPR. Candidates often find difficulty with demonstrating leadership because of an inability to recognise it within their own career development. The Review process acknowledges that certain leadership roles will only come with professional qualification and experience. Therefore the expectations of the Reviewers will be tempered to what can reasonably be expected of engineers approaching their Reviews. However, remember what many Reviewers will be asking themselves, 'Will this person, when placed in a position of responsibility, make the right decision?'. You must therefore have been exposed to leadership challenges and be able to demonstrate that you acquitted yourself appropriately. Leadership does not necessarily require you to have led large numbers of people; it can be demonstrated in a variety of ways. It is up to you to identify the right occasions and describe them.

Clearly indicate your role in any relevant aspects of the projects, giving background to important decisions you were responsible for, or made a significant contribution to

This requirement provides you with an opportunity to demonstrate your achievements at the required level to satisfy the Attributes. In addressing this requirement you will be able to cover a good deal of ground and explain how you have undertaken the role of a professional engineer at the requisite level. We have explained earlier that engineers are often poor at recognising the application of their own skills. Furthermore, there are many members of our profession who are poor at selling themselves. This is your opportunity to convince the Reviewers of your abilities. For example, a particular design might have required the engineer to consider matters of sustainability, health and safety and cost simultaneously. Combining several Attribute requirements into one thread of your professional life is an effective way of proving your worth to the Reviewers.

Show where you exercised independent judgement

Probably the most important component of the Report, this is one of the most difficult issues to demonstrate. Without having been exposed to the situation of exercising independent judgement you will not be able to pass either the MPR or the CPR. You have to explain the background to the Reviewers in a manner that enables them to understand it while still appreciating the complexity of the task you undertook. A significant number of failed candidates at the Reviews have not addressed this requirement adequately.

A brief, two-page CV

The brief CV is a vital component of your submission and is likely to be the first document that your Reviewers examine. You should pay heed to the page limit and not resort to obvious moves such as using a small font. No matter how much you consider your application to be a special case, your CV should not be longer than the two-page limit. When each of us applied for Fellowship, we both had considerable periods of extensive experience but were still able to get it all onto one page by being very clear about what we were trying to prove.

Reviewers have remarked to us how highly they value this element of the submission. If your CV exceeds the clearly stated limit then the Reviewers are likely to draw early conclusions about your abilities. This CV is completely different from one that you might use to obtain a new job or that used by many employers to sell their services. If constructed carefully, you can save word count to utilise later. For example:

> Section Engineer – Bridges, responsible for the dimensional and quality control
> and construction of 4 motorway overbridges on the £380 M A1 Leeming to
> Barton Improvement procured using the NEC3 Engineering & Construction
> Contract Main Option C

tells the Reviewers what you were doing on that site and informs them of the role, value, project name, your duties, etc. all in a document which is *not* included in the total word count. Then, when you refer to the 'A1 project' in the main body of the Report (where the word count *does* apply), the Reviewers will know the context.

Successful Professional Reviews for Civil Engineers
ISBN 978-0-7277-6100-2

ICE Publishing: All rights reserved
http://dx.doi.org/10.1680/sprce61002.069

Institution of Civil Engineers

publishing

Chapter 11
Reports – common faults

Underplaying your hand

Many Reports that we have read, as mentors and Reviewers, have underplayed the writer's hand; there seems to be a reluctance to spell out just exactly what you did and understood, expecting the Reviewers to 'read between the lines' to decide for themselves. This is not good enough – you must *demonstrate* your abilities, not assume they can be tacitly inferred. It is not generally in an engineer's character to boast but, in this instance, you must try! It is also difficult to admit to mistakes, yet these are often where good experience was gained. The Reviewers will be less interested in the mistake than in what you did to rectify it and what you learnt from it.

Why do most candidates underplay their hand? We think it is due to one fundamental reason. Engineers are problem solvers; once a problem is resolved and a solution found, they go on either to solve the problems of implementation or to another problem. In other words, they forget the original problem. So, to write the Report successfully requires you to remember the solution and then unravel the thinking behind your decisions to fully expose the original problem.

The difficulty only increases the more experience you have, because you may then know how to solve a recurring problem, which means it is no longer a problem *to you*. But, in fact, it remains a problem, allowing you to demonstrate how your experience enabled you to solve it.

Another difficulty is that we all know that, in reality, none of us works in isolation. Everything we do we discuss with others. As a result, we are loathe to take personal credit for our work. But ask yourself who would have taken the blame if things had gone wrong – if it was you, then you were personally responsible, however many people you discussed the problem with.

Failing to demonstrate competence

Every time you mention that something was done or happened, immediately follow with 'because ...' and 'What else was considered and why were the alternatives rejected?'. This will compel you to explain your precise role in the process more accurately. Your Reviewers are interested not so much in what was done, as in why and how and what part you played in those decisions.

Be prepared to put yourself on the line and tell the Reviewers that, with hindsight, you now believe that there might have been a better solution (after all, one of the things you must demonstrate is the ability to learn from experience). Even where the decisions were not yours to take, you can state that you offered advice, collected information, thought of ideas or suggestions or made recommendations which were subsequently accepted. You may even have drafted the instruction, email, report or similar documentation for someone else to sign – say so! And where you had no direct involvement, you must show that you understand how the decision was reached; after all, it will not be long until you are making comparable decisions as a professional engineer. It is always better to have some experience *before* decisions need to be made than afterwards!

An example:

> The bridge was designed by [the candidate's consultancy] as a continuous, twin-celled cast in-situ reinforced concrete deck supported on piers with piled foundations and two spread footing abutments. The contractor proposed an alternative single-celled design in his tender which the employer accepted.

What a wasted opportunity! And, perhaps, a tacit suggestion that the candidate's original design had not been sufficiently thought through? We think the Reviewers are almost bound to ask, 'Was that not something you considered at preliminary design stage?'. The candidate must know why the original format was chosen, what alternatives were rejected and whether one of them was a single-celled design. Why was the decision apparently so readily changed when the contractor offered the alternative? The candidate may not even agree with the decisions, but must explain their understanding of them.

We are often told by candidates that the reason such explanations are not included is because they have been advised to leave questions hanging for the Reviewers to ask. We strongly advise that such a deliberate approach is mistaken, for two reasons:

(*a*) the prescribed length of the Reports is too short to include everything, so there will inevitably be unanswered questions without any deliberate attempt to pose them
(*b*) the Reviewers are wily enough to recognise a 'trailing coat' when they see one and will probably avoid it, because they know that you know the answer! There will be plenty of other questions which are not 'flagged up' so blatantly.

Another example of a case where the candidate hopelessly failed to demonstrate their competence:

> The piled foundations for each of the piers consisted of driven vertical and raked steel H piles founding at varying depths across the valley. In addition to the seven permanent

piers, eight temporary piers were erected in between the permanent piers, again supported on steel H piles. Thus I gained much experience monitoring piling operations.

When Mac reviewed the candidate, he found out that he had, in fact, devised a neat and simple device to aid the checking of the required sets on so many piles, thus saving hours of laborious and repetitive work. Yet he made no mention of this in the Report. His last sentence was wasted.

Writing in the third person

Many engineers have written reports for committees or clients, or for an academic forum, where writing passively in the third person is invariably required. There is frequently a tendency to write these submission reports in a similar manner as a result of such experience. The worst scenario is exemplified here, from a candidate reviewed by Patrick:

The construction of the control room was undertaken off site and delivered to the site in modules which were then assembled together on site by a subcontract team. The design of the modules had to be undertaken to allow for the transport to site and for the erection on site. A detailed risk assessment and method statement had to be prepared for the site operations, allowing for the potential influence of the weather.

The candidate who wrote this passage did not claim credit for anything. As Reviewers we were left uninformed about her actual role here. Only after interviewing her did Patrick find (after some difficulty) that she had undertaken most of the activities referred to. She would have been better advised to have used active verbs to explain what she did.

Remember the underlying purpose. Rewrite as:

The control room was fabricated off site by our subcontractor. I led a team of three designers to produce the design of the modules. This design allowed for the transport to site and for the erection on site. My design included a detailed risk assessment and method statement for the site assembly, allowing for the potential influence of the weather.

The length of the sentence has been decreased but, much more importantly, your responsibility is now *demonstrated*.

Another common mistake relates to the manner in which you write. We can almost guarantee that you will repeat the most common error of all – you will say, 'I was involved in ...' or 'I was responsible for ...'. To avoid these vague generalisations, *always* turn the sentences around to force you to be more specific – 'My involvement included ...' and 'My responsibilities were ...'.

Other very common understatements include phrases such as 'I was then transferred to ...' or 'Once I had been given the task of ...'. How much more positive it sounds and how much more in control you appear to be, if these are rephrased as 'I then transferred to ...', 'I had the task of ...' or even better 'I did ...'. And the changes actually save words.

Use of abbreviations

Use acronyms whenever you can to keep the Report short, but always tell the reader what the letters mean the first time they are mentioned. For example, what exactly is PMI? Those working with the NEC Engineering and Construction Contract will know that it is a Project Manager's Instruction, but you should not assume that everyone else does. All sections of the industry and even individual projects develop their own vocabulary and you should define everything at first use. You might expect everyone to know, but you cannot assume that they do. There is another important point to be made here; even once you have defined what PMI means, you will need to explain what it is and how it was used in your work.

Be careful that your abbreviations and acronyms are correct; perhaps you could include a glossary in your submission, though it may be included in the word count for the Report.

Jargon

Avoid jargon! We all use it every day as part of our communication at work, but in formal documentary communication it is unacceptable. Here is a classic example, where there is not one genuine engineering term in the whole sentence:

> The rebar cage was prefabbed outside the hole and craned in just before the RE's inspection so that the rubbish could be removed easily from the shutters.

Such use of jargon is completely unacceptable. But worse – there is an implication here that perhaps the cleaning would not have been done at all but for the RE's inspection. So it is absolutely vital that you read and comprehend exactly what your sentences say, not what you think or believe they say! This version is much better, and uses fewer, more appropriate words:

> The reinforcement was prefabricated alongside the excavation and lifted in after the formwork had been thoroughly cleaned and prepared.

There is no need to mention the RE, and this is a dated term nowadays anyway; the cleaning would have been done in any case, because you must demonstrate that you have a professional attitude.

Another source of annoyance to some Reviewers is the use of new words which are creeping into the workplace: words such as optioneering and buildability. Until they are in the dictionary, try not to use them. Why irritate those whom you are trying to convince?

Grammar and syntax

Even when you have edited the draft to something like the correct length and made sure that every sentence addresses the objective of demonstrating that you are a professional engineer, the task is by no means complete. Now you have to start checking the spelling, punctuation, grammar and syntax. Some people are not clear about what grammar and syntax are. Remember the simple description:

- grammar is the correct words
- syntax is the correct words in the correct order.

If you have difficulties with any of these, do not tempt fate by being too adventurous. Like Winston Churchill, who admitted to early difficulty with the English language, just keep your sentences short and your words simple; only use full stops and commas. Even though the Institution has advised the Reviewers that they should not penalise a candidate for failures in the education system, we think this is going too far, and would strongly advise that you master the use of the possessive apostrophe, or just avoid having to use it.

It is very difficult to read your own work and find errors, because you tend to read what you want it to say, rather than what it actually says. You also know what you are trying to say, whereas someone reading it for the first time does not. So you have to try to detach yourself and read the Report as a third person. To help, it is also a good idea to get others, engineers who do not know anything about your experience and even people who are not engineers, to read it. They will ask questions which cause you to query whether what you have written expresses exactly what you intended.

Checking spelling is something else which requires great care and time; it needs to be done as a separate exercise, where you do not actually read the Report, but only check the spelling, punctuation and syntax. You cannot rely on your computer's spell- or grammar-checking capabilities, which are limited and usually cannot tell the difference between 'right' and 'write', 'their' and 'there', etc. There is a poem on the internet (*Ode to the Spellchecker*) which goes through most spellcheckers with no changes at all:

I halve a spelling checker,
it came with my Pea Sea
it plainly marques for my revue
miss steaks eye kin knot sea.

I strike a key and type a word
and weight four it two say
weather eye am wrong or write
it shows me strait a weigh.

As soon as a mist ache is maid
it nose bee for two long
and eye can put the error rite
its rare lea ever wrong.

Eye halve run this poem threw it
eye am shore your pleased two no
its let her perfect awl the weigh
my checker tolled me sew.

You need to be very painstaking – the following example is a classic, which at least six people who read the Report before submission failed to notice:

This meant that both pupils and their parents were forced to cross a very busy dual carnageway.

If you needed a double-take to spot the error, this merely demonstrates how difficult checking is!

Do spread your checking beyond the Report itself, to the cover sheet and picture captions. It is not sensible to have a cover sheet which announces in two-centimetre-high letters that your submission is for the

CHARTERED PROFESSIONAL REVUE

or that your project report describes a

LARGE SCALE DEWARTING SYSTEM

or, and this is setting you up for a difficult Review day, that you are applying to the

INSTITUTE OF CIVIL ENGINEERING

all of which appeared at the Institution!

Summary

By now we hope you have realised that the compilation of the Report is not easy. It is our considered view that there is a fundamental need for time in this process, though it often elicits a surprised response when we suggest that at least four months is a reasonable minimum. There is no substitute for reflection – setting aside the Report for a few days and looking at it again with fresh eyes. You also need to ask as many others as you reasonably can to read your work – and not only other engineers. They will all offer different suggestions, but at least they will have caused you to look at the Report in different ways. You can then make up your own mind as to which suggestions you take and which you discard.

Since, in theory, you have infinite time and infinite support and resources to prepare the Report, the Institution expects it to be perfect, just as any professional report emanating from your office should be. Those for whom English is not their first language are expected to demonstrate that, as potential professionally qualified engineers, they have recognised a possible problem and taken appropriate steps to ensure that their Reports are well-presented by asking someone with a sound knowledge of English to correct any errors.

Whenever we ask candidates after their Review if they have any advice on the Report for future candidates, their response is invariably 'I wish I had allowed myself more time'. A well-written Report does take time and effort, but it will probably make your interview less onerous, getting your Review off to a good start.

Successful Professional Reviews for Civil Engineers
ISBN 978-0-7277-6100-2

ICE Publishing: All rights reserved
http://dx.doi.org/10.1680/sprce61002.077

Chapter 12
Supporting documents

Mention of the supporting documents to your Professional Review Report has been made already since, as we explained in Chapter 4, it is impossible to separate any one part of the submission from the others; the pieces of the jigsaw must interlock to form a complete picture.

The *Professional Review Guidance* document states that 'numerical analyses, cost data, drawings or other relevant additional documentation should be included as appendices to support the content of your report'. The aim is to provide supporting evidence which:

- assists in demonstrating the abilities being displayed in your Report
- justifies and supports the decisions which you mention in the Report.

Careful choice is necessary; the Reviewers are not impressed by sheer bulk. Indeed, one Reviewer deliberately collected statistics over many years with which he created a probability curve which showed clearly that

the success of a submission is inversely proportional to its size.

The Institution has made many attempts to limit the size of candidates' submissions over the years; a weight limit was imposed during the years of hard copy submissions through the postal system. The current rules are, in our view, the most sensible yet and limit you to the following:

- three drawings, which should be legible when printed at A3 size and relevant to your Report
- twelve A4 sides of additional information, including any relevant calculations.

Rules such as these should be adhered to; it is highly unlikely that your Reviewers will consider you to be a special case worthy of preferential treatment. Think carefully about the drawings you choose to submit and consider the possibility that one or both of your Reviewers may lack the hardware to print A3 drawings. In our experience, it is highly improbable that any A0 or similar sized drawings can be reduced to A3 and still be readable, unless they have been specially drafted for this purpose. Do not fall into the trap of trying to compress working drawings in this way. Far better to produce detail sketches at the size you choose, perhaps A4 (bearing in mind that most Reviewers will have only a small printer at home).

The inclusion of every document must be a considered decision; does it contribute positively to the overall objective – to prove you are a professional engineer? If it does not, then discard it.

Analyses

These must demonstrate that your decisions (or the decisions taken by your line management, but to which you contributed) are based on sound knowledge and understanding. They need not necessarily be engineering analyses, but could just as readily be commercial or economic.

Detailed analysis is not design, but is an integral, indeed vital, part of the design process and generally takes place towards the end, when you are justifying the solution you have chosen and making sure it will withstand the forces and loading conditions you have decided it must resist. Prior to that, analysis (generally using quick design methods) helps in the choice of the most appropriate solution.

Documentary evidence is needed for the Reviewers to ratify technical competence if they feel it necessary. They are much more interested in how the calculations were used as an integral and vital part of solving a problem or implementing a solution. The purpose is to *demonstrate* your understanding of technical (or scientific for Associates) principles, not that you can 'do calculations'!

Do not rewrite calculations specially for use in the submission; documents should have been prepared 'during the normal course of your work'. Do not abstract aborted calculations; they were an integral part of the design process, vital in choosing the most appropriate solution. Do select only those (generally at the beginning) which show that you know how the loading conditions and design criteria were chosen, even where they were established by others – be prepared to answer such questions as 'Why was this designed for a 1-in-25-year storm?', 'Why did you consider earthquake loadings?' or 'Why was the bridge designed as an integral structure?'. It is answers to such questions as these which enable you to demonstrate your understanding. Too often the calculations submitted merely show that the candidate can follow the methodology in a design manual.

Those of you who are not involved in the detailed design process will see that the answers to the questions posed above do not require you to be directly involved. You can demonstrate your understanding of the technical principles underlying the work with which you are involved, knowing the answers without doing the calculations.

As long as your calculations are neat and legible (even a few crossings out are acceptable), you state where new figures or numbers came from and explain why you did them that way by annotating the calculations appropriately with cross-references, the Reviewers will be able to see clearly that, not only did you do the calculations, but also that

you understand what the calculations are doing.

Many calculations are done by computer. The Reviewers do not wish to see reams of printout, but need answers to questions such as:

- What assumptions were made or are inherent in the computer program?
- How did you satisfy yourself that those assumptions were valid for your problem?
- What assumptions did you make in order to ensure that your problem would fit the program?
- With hindsight, was the method or program you used the most appropriate?

And, the most important of all:

- How did you satisfy yourself that the results were realistic?

These sorts of questions make it quite clear that calculations are a means to an end rather than an end in themselves. You must *demonstrate* how the calculations were used to solve problems such as deciding on alternative structural forms, sizing and reinforcement of members, choice of materials or the most appropriate construction methods and plant. For construction method statements, for example, you will probably have had to consider temporary stability.

In all calculations, assumptions are made about the value of constants and factors. If you, for example, used a value for Young's modulus or a factor of safety, then do be prepared to discuss why it was deemed appropriate. It may not have been your decision this time, but in the future, as a qualified professional engineer, you will be required to make similar decisions. You must demonstrate that you can!

Cost data

A conventional cost estimate, activity schedule or bill of quantities might be one vehicle by which to *demonstrate* an understanding of construction methods and the financial implications of the solution, but only if it is used properly. The compilation itself reveals little or nothing about your competence as a professional engineer, only your methodical administration.

Such a document should demonstrate your understanding of rates and item coverage – the 'build-up'. It is important that you do more than reuse previous rates from other estimates or quotations so that you demonstrate your understanding of how the rates were adjusted to suit your particular job, or what a rate includes – item coverage. You would not have to be a professional engineer to copy previous rates into a new bill, but we are not at all sure the result would actually be realistic.

The job for which the cost estimate is compiled need not necessarily be a construction project; it could be, for example, the manufacture of apparatus or equipment, or a proposed traffic count.

Other possibilities might include:

- the substantiation of a claim
- the estimate for a variation requested by the client or their agent
- the build-up of an estimate for a proposal
- an estimate of design costs, including the build-up of rates.

Illustrations

Use drawings throughout your submission to save words – 'one picture is worth a thousand words'.

Another example:

I was temporarily seconded to this site as the Supervisor. The works at this site were part of several 'Advance Works' contracts for major improvement works to a busy road junction over and adjacent to the Metro system. These particular works consisted of the construction of a pedestrian/cycleway ramp and associated retaining wall from an existing bridge over the underground lines to an anchored sheet pile wall at the entrance to a future subway under a road adjacent to the works.

Can you visualise the site? It is crying out for a diagram. Not a copy of the highway map, which would present far too much detailed information, but an outline sketch.

And look at the wasted words: surely a secondment can only be temporary? And there are no less than five references to 'the works' in only two overlong sentences – the candidate obviously never read the report aloud! A sketch and drastic editing could release many words for telling the Reviewers how the candidate benefited from the experience at this complicated site.

As mentioned above, many candidates still make the mistake of using contract drawings. We believe it is much better to use simplified extracts from them or the sort of simple diagrams favoured by those who prepare publicity material. After all, contract drawings are required to transmit detailed and accurate contractual information, generally far too detailed for the purpose of your Report. In all the many submissions we have seen:

> we have yet to find a valid reason for including contract drawings in a submission.

There has invariably been a better option.

Since the Reviewers have to assimilate the information quickly as an adjunct to your experience, they do not want to have to unravel a complicated drawing to glean the basic information they need. To assist them, we suggest that you put pictures and sketches within the text, alongside the part of the report to which they refer; word processing software makes this relatively straightforward. Where you do choose to include photographs, drawings, etc. then annotate them to make the desired message absolutely apparent.

Other kinds of illustrations might include, for example:

- photographs
- architect's 'impressions'
- extracts from explanatory leaflets for public circulation.

Be careful in your choice of the first of these. Photographs have rarely been taken for the purpose of the Review (unless you have been planning well ahead) and so are inevitably second best. Do not be tempted to include a photograph merely because it is the best you have. Keep asking: does it help the Reviewers to understand the situation? Mac clearly remembers a photograph of a bright blue waterproofed bridge deck, with a faint line across it, titled 'The expansion joint'. The potential candidate confessed, 'It's the only photograph I have of the deck joint'. He was persuaded that it was useless to the Reviewers, so he substituted a sketched cross-section of the expansion joint.

Drawing is a common method of communication for engineers. So demonstrate that you can visualise an engineering problem (spatial awareness) by including drawings and sketches (not necessarily exactly to scale or drawn with a straight-edge) where you thought out a design, technical or construction problem or transmitted information (e.g. to CAD or to the subcontractor or designer, or to someone manufacturing apparatus).

> You *will* be expected to draw during your interview – paper and pencil are provided.

However, we would recommend that you take a felt-tipped pen or similar to the interview, since pencil lines are sometimes difficult to see across a table.

Look very carefully at every illustration. First, to be sure that it does actually contribute towards the overall objectives, either:

- demonstrating that you are a professional engineer, or
- reducing the word count.

Second, look very carefully at the background to every picture: is there anything there which you would rather not show? Even professional journals have frequently been criticised for using pictures where something inappropriate is going on in the background. Too often, photographs open up discussions on peripheral matters, such as safety or efficiency, which can take you unawares.

Passport photograph

You are required to include a recent photograph on the front cover of your Professional Review Report. This is used by the Reviewers as an aid to remembering exactly which candidate was which. But do have the photograph taken when the Review is imminent. Changing the style or colour of your hair or wearing contact lenses on the day when your photograph shows you wearing spectacles can cause (and has caused) confusion. A picture of you in hard hat and fluorescent jacket with the collar turned up may show you at work, but is not particularly useful in identifying you as the person at the interview.

Summary

As far as possible, try to incorporate the supporting documents in such a way that the Reviewer can easily be directed to them at the same time as continuing to read the report – the use of hyperlinks, for example, makes this easy. Obviously, if the link to the supporting document is a substitute for a written description to save on the word count, then it should be incorporated into the text whenever possible, but a few pages of appendix giving more detailed justification for a technical or financial decision is better at the back.

Minimise your supporting documents. Never include repetitive calculations: the Reviewers are not going to check whether you can do arithmetic! They are far more interested in how and why you did the calculations, and what values you chose for any constants, load cases, factors of safety or profit margins.

Successful Professional Reviews for Civil Engineers
ISBN 978-0-7277-6100-2

ICE Publishing: All rights reserved
http://dx.doi.org/10.1680/sprce61002.083

Chapter 13
Putting the Professional Review submission together

The requirements for the Professional Review submission

By now you have compiled four of the seven pieces of your jigsaw and the picture should be becoming clear. Now is the time to finally make sure that all these pieces interlock without either gaps or overlaps. Each document should stand alone as a complete entity, but be referenced to the others. Supporting documents should be rechecked to make certain that they really do *support* your case or provide the Reviewers with essential background information. It is at this stage that many candidates will be frantically saying:

'My submission is way over 20MB!'.

What these candidates have done is to put all the pieces together and frightened themselves because they have only scanned, rather than read and understood, the specification.

The Institution's requirements for the submission to the Reviewers are:

- a cover page/contents
- a two-page CV
- the Professional Review Report
- appendices
- CPD records.

File submission rules

Your Professional Review submission must be:

- one self-contained PDF file
- A4 sized (but A3 allowed for drawings – however, see our comments in Chapter 12)
- no larger than 20MB
- filename as specified by the Institution (at the time of writing, 2015, this is to be your ICE member number, initials, surname and review date – for example, 12345678_G.SPRAKE_17.10.15).

Structuring and designing your Professional Review submission

These rules should be relatively straightforward to satisfy. Use technology to your advantage and illustrate, annotate and apply hyperlinks wherever desirable. If you lack the confidence to use software to a sufficiently high standard then you should seek help from others. A clearly presented package that is easy to use will work in your favour with the Reviewers. Their first impression of you will be a good one and will set you off to a good start.

Completing your submission in under 20MB requires a combination of two tasks:

- the use of the right software and technology to make your document appear professional, while staying under the file size limit
- selecting the right materials to include in your submission, taking care to demonstrate the Attributes without unnecessary padding.

If you get these two tasks right, it is our experience that,

> properly focused submissions do not approach the limit.

The rules may not always be rigidly enforced but you should approach this task with the assumption that they will be. Getting a 20MB submission through at least two different email systems may prove to be a challenge so you certainly should not exceed this limit.

Discussing the submission leads us to another point: it is a good idea to draw up a table of who requires each document, so that you can readily see who needs what. We have compiled this one for MPR/CPR at the time of writing (2015). It is up to you to check that the rules have not changed since then.

Document	Initial application	Professional Review submission	Self – for reference and file
Application form	1		1
Fee[1]	1		1
Sponsor forms[2]	3		
Academic qualifications proof[3]	1		1
IPD proof	1		1
Précis of Professional Review Report	1		1
CV	1		1
Evidence of special requirements[3]	1		1
Cover page/contents		1	1
Two-page CV		1	1
Professional Review Report		1	1

Document	Initial application	Professional Review submission	Self – for reference and file
Appendices	1		1
Development Action Plan	1		1
Personal Development Record	1		1

Notes:
1. Proof of payment.
2. To be sent to the Institution directly by the sponsors.
3. If necessary.

Conflict of interest

You are given about four weeks' notice of your Review date. In the same letter/email, you are given the names of your two Reviewers. With your Lead Sponsor, who probably has a wider perspective, check that there can be no possibility of any conflict of interest, such as your respective employers being in serious contractual dispute or perhaps simply that you have met previously. Do not be afraid to bring any conflict of interest to the attention of the ICE Reviews Manager. It is probable that the Reviewer concerned has already done the same, although the Reviewers will probably have been told of your identity before you knew of theirs.

Covering letter

Submit your document to the Institution as soon after receipt of the letter as possible. The minimum requirement is to allow fifteen working days before your interview. But it surely creates a good impression of organisation and control if you get your submission to your Reviewers sooner, particularly bearing in mind that they are going to read the documents in their own time.

Your organisation would probably not send any documents to a client without a covering letter. Yet many submissions do arrive cold and unannounced. Include a letter, addressed to the Reviewers in which you say that your submission is attached in accordance with the rules, draw their attention to any deviations from the rules and the reasons for them and, in the final paragraph, say that you are looking forward to meeting them at the prearranged date and time. This will prompt them to check that their information agrees with yours and removes the possibility of any error.

Make absolutely certain that you use the Reviewers' names and qualifications on your letter exactly as you were given them. There is nothing more annoying than receiving a letter that is incorrectly addressed or with your name misspelt and, because of its familiarity, it is something which the recipient notices immediately. Take the Reviews

Department letter with you so that, if a Reviewer does complain, you can show them precisely what information you were given.

Waiting

It seems an eternity from the final date of submission to your interview. This is the time to look ahead, to try to anticipate how the remaining pieces might be compiled. You are not totally in control of these but, as far as possible, you must reduce the chances of the unexpected. For example, you should be able, perhaps with help from other people in the office, to make a realistic guess as to what topics might be covered in the Written Exercise, since it will be based on your own personal experience.

Researching the Reviewers

It is always a temptation to try to find out who your Reviewers are and what their particular areas of expertise might be. This is, perhaps, an understandable effort to remove yet another uncertainty. Most people, particularly those in professional roles, can be found on the internet and it may be useful background information to discover what your Reviewers do for a living. In reality, however, this is unlikely to materially improve your chances of passing the Review.

The reasoning is straightforward. Your Reviewers have been chosen for their expertise as *Reviewers* and not particularly because they are able, from their own particular field of work, to ask searching technical questions. Remember the purpose of the Review – to explore whether you have become a professional engineer, not whether you are technically competent.

All the Reviewers are volunteers, who serve the Institution in their own time and largely at their own expense, apart from travelling and accommodation expenses. They do it for two reasons: one is their professional responsibility and a desire to serve their Institution in a tangible way, the other is that they genuinely enjoy meeting 'the next generation' and really look forward to successful Reviews. The one thing they do not want is an unsuccessful Review!

Most were trained themselves some years ago and all have an interest in training and development and the maintenance of the Institution's reputation for excellence. The Institution is very proud and protective of its Reviewers, who are subject to continual monitoring and review themselves.

All potential reviewers go through quite a lengthy process of training, at any stage of which the Institution may decide not to appoint that person to the panel. All Reviewers are required to undergo formal training at least every three years; most, in fact, do rather more than this minimum. And many are recruited as young as their thirties – so don't presume your Reviewers are inevitably going to be old.

The difficulties in researching your particular Reviewers come when you perhaps find out that one has a reputation (probably totally false, because you cannot possibly sample a representative group of their candidates) for a particular line of questioning and you become obsessed with that to the detriment of other aspects. The interview will, almost certainly, be perversely different! Or you might hear that a Reviewer is particularly aggressive (again, probably without any real justification) – how is that going to affect your build-up? Hardly likely to give you confidence, is it? Having watched and partici-pated for several years, we know that most Reviewers do, in practice, change their style slightly to suit each particular candidate.

Of far greater significance, after submitting your documents, is deciding how to make the presentation and what it should cover.

Successful Professional Reviews for Civil Engineers
ISBN 978-0-7277-6100-2

ICE Publishing: All rights reserved
http://dx.doi.org/10.1680/sprce61002.089

Chapter 14
Preparing for the presentation

The presentation is the key element locking the submission documents to the interview. It is your great opportunity to influence the whole Review process; it will occupy about a quarter of the interview and could well determine the shape, content and style of the remainder. It is the first opportunity for you to actually show yourself operating as a professional engineer rather than writing about yourself.

The need for a presentation

Why do the Reviewers need a presentation when they already have so much information from your submission? The interview is *your* chance to strengthen your case and the Reviewers expect you to do most of the talking, with them only directing you to those matters they would like you to cover.

The Reviewers learn much about you from your presentation, particularly whether you can inspire confidence, i.e. create the impression that you are passionate and committed about your work and really understand the full effects of what you are doing. The Institution is well aware that many of us have to justify our decisions in a variety of public situations – exhibitions, enquiries, committees and, possibly, in courts of law. So you are expected to show that you could cope in such circumstances. Of course you will be nervous: we all are, even the Reviewers! It is how you control those nerves that matters.

This part of the Review is meant to replicate the sort of presentation you will be expected to make as a professional engineer when putting proposals to a client. You will have sent them documents beforehand, but would follow these up with a visit to draw their attention to the key issues and why you believe your organisation is the best one to undertake the work. So, in this case, the purpose of your presentation is to draw the Reviewers' attention to those aspects of your Report where you displayed your full ability, and convince them that you really are a professional engineer.

In fifteen minutes, it is highly unlikely that you could cover all of your Professional Review Report, nor are you expected to. So the first step is to decide which part or parts you are going to amplify. What could you best use to reinforce your demonstration of the Attributes? It's back to the list of Attributes to help in the decision. Very often it is a (perhaps relatively small) contentious issue where you had to decide on the best course of action and then explain to several others why you made that decision. You need to quickly sketch in the problem and then move on to pick out the key points in the work which *demonstrate* your skills and abilities and reinforce them.

Do start your presentation by telling the Reviewers what you have decided and perhaps why. Knowing how the presentation will flow will make them feel more comfortable.

Presentation material

You can use almost anything – so long as it is appropriate and makes a positive contribution to the fundamental aim of the Review – to demonstrate the full range of your capabilities. Remember, you are going to talk to two people sitting down across a small table. We do strongly recommend you to use something for them to look at – anything which will prevent the Reviewers spending the whole fifteen minutes staring at you, which can be very disconcerting.

The almost universal aid is an A3 or A4 flipchart, with pictures and diagrams on the Reviewers' side and bullet points on the back as an aide-memoire. We have formed the opinion that A3 is, in fact, too large and an A4 flipchart is more appropriate. There is no doubt, however, that a flipchart is a convenient way of keeping yourself on track, both with content and timing. The other big advantage of an A4 format is that it will go into your briefcase or backpack, thus giving you one less thing to carry.

Many of the presentations we have seen have used far too much material – far too much writing, too many photographs on one display, too many page displays. After all, you are expecting the Reviewers to assimilate the visual information virtually instantly as an adjunct to what you are telling them, so they cannot realistically be expected to take in much.

How many displays should there be? A rule of thumb is no more than one every minute, i.e. no more than fifteen in a fifteen-minute presentation (not including the front cover).

Too often, visual aids are compiled to assist the presenter, rather than the Reviewers. When being coached as a lecturer, Mac was told, 'If you have to resort to words on a visual, never more than four lines, never more than three words to a line'. A maximum of twelve words on a display – not a great deal of scope. But if you look at advertising hoardings, they do not seem to stray far from that advice.

In the Review scenario, we would suggest that the use of video is inappropriate although it has been tried. To our knowledge, no one has yet tried an iPad or similar device but, again, it would be too small for two people, sitting on the opposite side of the table, to see. Neither are contract drawings much use; unfolding them does not cause too many problems, but folding them back up certainly does. Candidates do tend to look as though they are trying to wallpaper the room.

There have been many problems with computers, and our advice is that the use of a PC, laptop, iPad or similar is unlikely to be as effective as a flip chart and also introduces the risk of technological difficulties into your presentation.

This does not mean that you cannot use a device, but you could be introducing undue complexity and unnecessary problems. Some of these potential pitfalls, based on several years' experience of the Review process, include the following.

- There is a temptation to use the software to the full, producing an 'all singing, all dancing' presentation. The Reviewers have found that this gets in the way of developing a relationship between themselves and the candidate, and this is the prime reason for our recommendation to avoid their use.
- Modern display screens are designed to be very directional, so that the person sitting next to you on the train or plane cannot see what you are doing. It is therefore difficult to adjust the screen so that it can be easily seen by both Reviewers, unless you use a widescreen model.
- Battery life (no power is available during the interview) is limited. How many times have you just had a little practice while waiting for the interview? Just how much battery life do you have left?
- The device needs to be switched on well before you are called to interview, otherwise you spend an inordinate amount of (your) time waiting. While you do have a stated start time, it is flexible and, luck being what it is, you may be called earlier than expected.

If you do decide to use a laptop, perhaps because you use one for presentations for work and it is a familiar technique, then think it through. Keep the visual content as simple as possible. Do not use animation. What would you do on the day if the technology failed? Presumably, take a hard copy back-up. If so, why not just use that instead, and avoid the complexities of a laptop?

More appropriate than a flipchart might be something to put on the desk. What that should be is best left to your imagination and creativity. We have seen all kinds of props:

- site plans, where a development progressed through a series of overlays, tracing the thought process that went into the design. If you use this technique, frame the original plan. It is almost impossible to fit an overlay exactly over the plan when your hands are unsteady, unless there is a frame to help
- two- and three-dimensional models, sometimes built up as part of the narrative
- pieces of rusty metal from an ailing structure

- a house brick
- a disc cut from a suspension cable
- a piece of experimental apparatus
- even a jar of some noxious effluent, the lid of which the candidate unscrewed at a key moment, to the amused discomfort of the Reviewers.

There is no requirement to take any visual aids at all. Mac has seen a candidate use nothing more than a felt tipped pen to draw on the scrap paper provided (try not to use the pencil provided – the lines are not dense enough to be seen easily across a table). That takes a certain amount of self-confidence, but for him it was a normal method of communication with architectural clients. He even drew his diagrams from the Reviewers' perspective!

The important thing is to make sure by adequate practice that you can effectively handle any props, even when very nervous. Fumbling about in an attempt to make something work will not inspire confidence.

This brings us to another point. You will, we hope, take documents with you in case specific questions are asked about matters which did not have supporting documents in the submission. If you need to refer to them, do make sure they are catalogued in some suitable order in your bag and that you have practised finding them. You do not want to spend great lengths of time bent double behind the desk, while the Reviewers wonder what you are doing. Again, take 'just enough'; be ruthless and discard anything which is not going to significantly reinforce your case – not 'just in case' but vital to your case.

The need for practice

Having decided what to include and how to present it and drafted a script, you must then practise. Even very famous and apparently effortless public speakers invariably practise. We know of one such speaker who *never* allows himself to be persuaded to make a speech without having prepared something first: perhaps not specifically for that occasion, but after many years' experience, he has sufficient base material and can adapt it to a rough outline in his mind in just a few minutes. He also regularly stands back from a full-length mirror and critically observes how he uses gestures and movements to reinforce his message, particularly before an important speech. Yet most observers believe he is a brilliant impromptu speaker who finds it easy to talk at any time on any matter. We do not think anyone ever really finds it easy, however long they have been doing it. But, done well, it can be very satisfying and very impressive.

The ideal place for you to practise is seated at a table with a mirror propped up in front of you so that your image in the mirror is about as far away as the Reviewers will be on the day. Look yourself in the eye, watch how you move and, particularly, see how you handle your visual aids. Speak out loud, pitch your voice at your reflection and time yourself. You will feel very self-conscious, but this is a good thing because it actually causes the adrenalin to flow, thus replicating the anxiety you will feel at the interview. Your timing is therefore likely to be about right.

Timing a talk cold or in your head is never successful; everybody goes rather ponderously in their mind whereas, in the real situation, you will either put in extra material and go even slower, or you will gabble and finish early. Which scenario applies to you? Only practice in real situations will enable you to find out.

If you intend to use some form of prompt, keep checking that the words on it are what you need; each time you are disconcerted during practice, see whether better keywords or a different layout would help, until your prompt is honed to perfection. We both believe that if you practice hard, you will have no need of a comprehensive prompt: perhaps just a list of the key points laid on the desk on a small card or on the back of your flipchart. This leaves your hands free to manipulate any visual aids.

Having done all this, get colleagues, relations – anyone – to listen to you. Mac well remembers one instance where the family dog got up and left the room when a candidate asked to practise his presentation! Seek opinions, criticism and advice – you do not need to take it all, but it will all help. Furthermore, you will become more confident and begin to relax a little.

Nevertheless, on the day, you *will* be nervous – this is a good thing! Actors will tell you that they have to be nervous to give a good performance; the day they become complacent is the day they leave the cast. What you must be able to do is control and conceal your nerves and the only way to accomplish this is to practise. Actors and good public speakers learn techniques for controlling their nerves – deep breathing, shaking and relaxing their limbs; there are all sorts of techniques which help. Throughout your previous training, you should have been taking every opportunity to speak in public so that you have developed these skills. If you have not done so, you need to practise and learn now.

Successful Professional Reviews for Civil Engineers
ISBN 978-0-7277-6100-2

ICE Publishing: All rights reserved
http://dx.doi.org/10.1680/sprce61002.095

Chapter 15
The Review day

The interview and Written Exercise are the first things which are not totally under your control. Four-sevenths of the jigsaw is entirely under your control and a further seventh, the presentation, is largely under your control. On that basis, it is difficult to understand how anyone can be unsuccessful if such a large proportion of the Review can be completed without any participation from your Reviewers!

What is likely to happen during the interview? The straightforward and obvious answer is 'Who knows?'. The Reviewers will by then have a broad plan of what they wish to cover (areas to be explored further) and will have decided on the titles for the Written Exercise, if that is required.

What they will not have is a list of specific questions which they intend to work through; they will play the interview by ear to a large extent, working from your presentation, their notes of any areas of your experience they wish to explore in greater depth and your reaction to their questions.

Nevertheless, there are many other uncertainties which can, and ought to, be removed. Any uncertainty breeds doubt and doubt fuels nerves, so the fewer uncertainties there are on the day, the better you are likely to perform.

Preliminaries

The first uncertainty is the journey – how and when you are going to get to the venue you chose on your submission form? If you are travelling the night before, have you arranged somewhere to stay? If at all possible, my advice would be to stay overnight close to the venue, unless you live sufficiently close not to have concerns about a punctual arrival.

Whatever arrangement you decide upon, it is sensible to do a reconnaissance. If you intend to travel on the morning of the Review, then do the same journey at roughly the same time on a weekday to gauge the traffic or the time required to make the trip by public transport. When stationary in a jam, it is comforting to know just how much longer it will take to arrive when you finally start to move again!

Visit the venue, perhaps in the session of Reviews preceding your own? Get the feel of the place and the atmosphere. Have a drink in the bar, find out what you can do (gym, swimming pool, sit in the park, etc.) between the interview and the Written Exercise. We even know of one successful candidate who went to the cinema. You should avoid the temptation to revise or do additional preparation between your interview and the Written Exercise. It is better that you have a break and clear your mind for the next stage. Sitting in your car or in a café 'revising the topics' merely makes you more tired and seems inevitably to remind you of all the things you do not know – definitely not the best way to prepare for the afternoon.

Appearance

The clue to the question of what to wear is the same as it has been for every aspect of the preparation – what are you trying to demonstrate: that you are a professional engineer. So look like one!

Our only criteria are that you should feel comfortable and enjoy whatever you are wearing; you do not want another uncertainty on the day. Do not wear something which you continually have to tug or adjust because you feel uncomfortable. Do not wear a skirt if you are more used to wearing trousers. Do not buy a dark formal suit if your style is somewhat more adventurous but, at the same time, bear in mind that the Reviewers expect you to project the image of a professional engineer.

Perhaps more importantly, what do your clients or the public expect? Most, we think, would expect a jacket but not necessarily a suit, normally with a subdued tie for men and modest neckline for women. Most engineers are a conservative lot, and do not particularly empathise with power dressing or strong fashion statements. Again, it is about judgement and the impression you are creating. Avoid distractions of all kinds – rattling jewellery, swaying earrings, a watch which beeps every quarter, anything which is going to become annoying in a tense atmosphere. Remember to turn off your phone.

The weather on the day may mean that you have to wear a coat or carry an umbrella. Leave them in the cloakroom to avoid the clutter which would otherwise result as you enter the interview room.

Arrival

There will be quite a lot of activity in the building on the day. There could be as many as a dozen Reviews all going on at the same time, so there will be upwards of 60 people directly involved in your 'round', and more from the one which is just ending.

Find the reception desk and book in as soon as you can, before finding the cloakroom (you should know where it is beforehand) and getting rid of everything you do not need.

Remember that the first thing that one of your Reviewers will do, after coming out to the reception area to invite you to join them, is to shake your hand – so keep your right hand free. Otherwise the very first visual contact you have will put you on the defensive, as you fiddle about getting flustered, trying to pick everything up and then changing everything around to shake hands. This is why we recommended in the paragraph above that you relieved yourself of any surplus baggage.

This reminds us of another vital point: nerves make us all want to go to the toilet, so make sure you go before, and do not feel the need during, the Review! You do not need any unnecessary distractions. Get back and sit in the waiting area about ten minutes before your due time; it is not unusual for the Reviewers to be running a few minutes early.

There is a strained atmosphere in the waiting area, since candidates deal with their nerves in differing ways; some babble continuously, some sit in a corner silently, others feel the need to walk about. Whatever you do, don't try to revise or go through your visual aids once again; it is too late.

In the waiting area, there are usually a couple of senior engineers strolling around, as well as the administrative team: a stand-by Reviewer, there in case of problems, and a member of the regional support team. They will talk to you, not with any ulterior motive, but merely to try to relax you. Everybody, from administrative staff to the Reviewers, is willing you to do well, and will do their best to assist you to do so.

One of your Reviewers will come out to the waiting area to get you. From that first moment of contact you are being observed. At least look as though you mean business, even if you feel awful. It may interest you to know that the Reviewers have usually only just met each other, so they are nearly as unfamiliar with each other as they are with you. Hopefully you have remembered both of their names (which you will have been told for submission of your documents) so even in the heat of the moment, you should not forget who they are. If one forgets to introduce you to their colleague, then introduce yourself to them – 'You must be . . .?'. Sometime during the interview, try to refer to each of them by name – it suggests you are in control of yourself and the situation.

During the short walk to the meeting desk, your Reviewer will talk informally, probably telling you a little of their own background and asking whether you have had a reasonable journey – anything to try to get you to relax. Talk to them! Don't just say, 'Yes, thank you' but have something in mind – 'Yes, but did you get stuck in that sewer replacement job in the High Street?' Such an answer shows that, even when under pressure you are interested in what is going on around you and had the foresight to anticipate possible delays – inspiring confidence. Even casual conversation is creating an impression and beginning to develop a relationship which *must* blossom and reach fruition in the next hour.

Interview scenario

This is your opportunity!

It is not for the Reviewers to find out your competence, but for you to demonstrate it.

The scenario is that you are approaching two existing members of the Institution and telling them that you have become their equivalent – a professional engineer. Their intimated response is 'Go on then, prove it!'.

Your table will be one of several, arranged round a large room in such a way that, as far as possible, candidates are not in eye contact with anyone other than their Reviewers. It sometimes happens that one of your senior staff, or someone you know, is acting as a Reviewer on the same day; if you know that this is a possibility, do inform the Institution and strenuous efforts will be made to ensure you are not in eye or sound contact with them. That is the last thing you need on such a stressful occasion.

Your two Reviewers will sit opposite you at an average-sized table (around 1.5 to 1.8 m × 1.0 m). There is not a lot of room for your visual aids after you add two or three drinks, two sets of open submission documents and some scrap paper and a pencil. As far as is practicable, the Reviewers sit facing into the room, with you facing the Reviewers with a wall behind them.

Water will be provided for you. Nerves will make your mouth dry, so be prepared and pour yourself a glass – always look in control.

Observers

There may be a fourth person sitting at one end of the desk, within your field of vision. They could be an observer from the Institution or the Engineering Council, as part of the quality assurance processes, or a new Reviewer learning by shadowing. They will take absolutely no part in the proceedings and have no influence on the outcome; you do not need to include them in your eye contact if you find it awkward. To all intents and purposes, they are 'virtual'.

Usually you will be asked beforehand by the administrators whether you mind the observer being present. There is no reason why you should not say 'Yes' if you feel particularly nervous; it certainly will not affect the conduct or result of the Review. If you object, the administrators will move that person somewhere else.

Presentation

Picture the scenario when deciding on how you will make your presentation and particularly when you practise, as you must if you are going to reduce all the uncertainties which otherwise surround this aspect of the day.

Video is not deemed appropriate for this intimate setting; you do not need a pointer or light pen and anything you use to illustrate your work should be to the scale of the setting – A3 maximum, certainly not A0 and, in our view, preferably A4. After all, there is an audience of two, not two hundred. The scene is informal and quite intimate. You will have to raise your voice slightly to overcome the ambient noise levels, but do not throw it as though you were talking to thousands: it is inappropriate and a distraction for everyone else.

How are you going to start? Do not introduce yourself again; they know who you are already. Too many candidates start in a loud voice, 'My name is . . .' or 'For my presentation today, I am going to . . .'. Not appropriate! Perhaps try, 'I know you will have read my Report so, for the next fifteen minutes, I am going to concentrate on (whatever it is you have decided to expand on)' or some similar phrase. Remember the old adage: tell them what you are going to tell them, tell them, and then quickly summarise what you have told them.

Make sure, if necessary by asking, that both Reviewers can see your visual aids. So often a candidate puts a flipchart on the left-hand corner of the desk, causing the Reviewer on the right-hand side to have to lean across to be able to see properly. Move your chair so that the things you are asking them to look at are centre stage during this formal part, but remember to move it back as you finish and you become the centre of interest.

Even though you will have practised many times, you must not give the impression of 'going through the motions'; your Reviewers will genuinely be interested, so do not dull their interest by boring them. You must inspire them with your enthusiasm.

At the end of your presentation, give your Reviewers a clue that you have come to the end: they may otherwise think that you are merely pausing to gather breath or have momentarily lost the thread. Close your presentation material, move your chair back to centre stage, and say, 'That is the end of my presentation. If you have any questions, I shall be pleased to answer them'.

Make sure you stay just within the time limit: anything longer will start to irritate the Reviewers, who are aware of how much ground remains to be covered in such a limited time. You are unlikely to get away with the tactic of extending your talk to reduce the questioning.

Interview questions

The questioning which follows the presentation is really a series of prompts to set you off talking again in a direction determined by the Reviewers, so do not give monosyllabic answers. They wish to see an engineer's mind at work, talking through problems and difficulties and discussing the judgements which have to be made every day of our working lives. The Reviewers talk about an '80/20 interview' – you talking for 80 per cent of the time, them using the remaining 20 per cent to direct you towards the areas they wish to explore further.

Do not be disconcerted if you are asked questions you cannot answer. We have discussed this with some Reviewers, who have told us that, occasionally, they do not know the answer either! What they want to see is what comes into your mind, how you tackle the question, what you would need to find out to arrive at an answer – in other words, what you do every time you are faced with an apparently insoluble problem at work.

As one Reviewer described it, 'Engineers stumble towards a solution in a relatively organised way! I would like to see the candidate doing just that'. This is why we counsel that the Review is very different from the conventional examinations that you have experienced up to now, where you have expected to give authoritative factual answers to any questions you have been asked. Engineering problems are not conducive to such black and white decisions. The Reviewers are anxious to see that you are capable of tackling complex problems, understanding the implications and using your judgement.

If you feel yourself coming under pressure, it is because you are not delivering what the Reviewers need to be convinced. They are not trying to catch you out, but attempting to get you to demonstrate some attribute which, as yet, they are unsure of. Try to detach yourself; become a third party and mentally step aside to see what it is that they really want. After all, you have convinced yourself and your sponsors that you are capable and competent, so you ought to feel confident that you are able to persuade these two fellow (or peer) engineers.

One of the things which really surprised both of us when we first became involved in the administration of the Reviews, was how much laughter emanates from the room, particularly towards the end of each batch of interviews, so don't be surprised if this happens.

The Reviewers really do enjoy meeting good candidates; for them a good morning consists only of successful Reviews. This is why most of them volunteer. They do not enjoy interviews where progress has been 'like drawing teeth' or meeting someone who was inadequately prepared or not up to standard. You would probably not enjoy that sort of interview either, so do not tempt fate!

Beware the quick throwaway question just as you relax – you are still under observation until you leave the room.

Guidance on developing the relationship

Until we get to know someone, our brains make snap judgements in an attempt to:

- categorise the person
- predict what they will do
- anticipate how we should react.

Whether we like to admit it or not, research shows that our brains make judgements about a person within milliseconds of meeting them – dictated by the evolutionary 'fight or flight' response. This inherent survival mechanism directs us to decide from how a person looks and behaves whether they are trustworthy, belligerent, competent, likeable and many other traits. Three of you (the Reviewers and yourself) are all making these assessments as soon as you meet.

Most of us are now circumspect with the conclusion of this process, having learnt that 'you cannot tell a book by its cover' or 'appearances are deceptive', so do not be too quick to make a firm decision.

Be aware of your own body language, mindful that it will influence the Reviewers' perception of you and possibly the outcome of the Review. Under pressure, we all make mistaken judgements, but their impact can be minimised if we are conscious of them. Here are a few suggestions from our observations of professional interviews.

Although you may not feel like smiling, failing to smile on introduction can make people uncomfortable, and your Reviewers may possibly wonder if you really want to be there. Try to give a genuine smile, especially when meeting your Reviewers for the first time. After all, in the next hour you are going to convince them that you can display all of your skills and abilities, so do try to look as though you are happy to communicate with them.

However, it is a professional occasion, so you should not become too relaxed. Leaning back casually in the chair can make you seem either lazy or arrogant. Wrapping your arm around the back of the chair might suggest that the Reviewer had been too successful in 'putting the candidate at their ease' and is definitely not recommended! On the other hand, leaning forwards, perhaps even with your elbows on the desk, can seem aggressive. Aim for a neutral posture, upright but comfortable. As a violinist, Mac was taught to hook his feet around the chair legs to keep him erect, a useful technique if you have a tendency to slouch.

Breaking eye contact too soon can make you seem overly nervous, perhaps even untrustworthy. Do hold eye contact just a fraction longer than you may ordinarily feel comfortable with, especially during a handshake. Conversely, staring for too long can be interpreted as aggressive or overbearing. Looking up or looking around too much can suggest that the candidate may be lying or not being themselves. Try to hold intermittent steady eye contact with both Reviewers in turn when delivering a response. There is a fine line between holding someone's gaze and staring them down but at least be aware of what you are doing.

Candidates' hands almost invariably cause difficulties. Think about what you will do with yours; watch yourself as you practise. Chopping or pointing with your fingers, as many politicians do in an attempt to look decisive, does seem aggressive from across a table, and can even create the impression that you are blustering to hide a deficiency.

Other candidates cross their arms, which makes them look defensive, especially when answering questions. You may see Reviewers doing the same, which can give you the impression that they are rejecting what you are saying to them. This is almost certainly not the case; for Mac, it is a way of taking the strain off his arthritic shoulders!

Definitely make a serious attempt not to fidget. We have both had candidates who actually tended to distract us from what they were saying by picking their nails, tugging at their clothing or fiddling with jewellery or a watch. Fidgeting instantly telegraphs the fact that you are nervous and is a distraction to those trying to get to know you. Avoid it at all costs.

To curb these hand movements, some candidates stuff their hands between themselves and the seat, or even deep in their pockets, which makes them look rigid and stiff. Aim for a natural posture, hands down by your sides or in your lap, which allows you to bring them up naturally to make a point.

So, to summarise, what should you do? Aim for good posture in a neutral position. Pay attention to your audience so that you naturally hold eye contact, smile and *be yourself*. If you discover you have a particular problem with one or two of the points to avoid on the list, practise by yourself with a mirror or with a friend who can remind you every time you do it, until you become aware of the bad habit yourself.

The interval

Try not to draw any conclusions from the way the interview went. First, you cannot really remember – it will all just be a blur. Second, if the Reviewers are good, they are unlikely to have revealed their thoughts and opinions, either about you, your ideas or your experience; so any conclusions you come to are based on very little factual evidence. We have encountered candidates who have burst into tears or become extremely angry, convinced they have failed, when, in fact, they did really well. Others have come out feeling very confident, only to get a letter eventually pointing out where they went horribly wrong.

You may, like a boxer, feel battered and bruised; just try to return for the next round – the written part – convinced you can deliver the knockout blow.

There is nothing to be gained by shutting yourself away in your car and mulling over everything that went wrong. Because this is what we fear you will do. It is the worst possible environment and the worst possible isolation.

Far better to join other candidates and talk, not about the interviews but about your work and experiences, last night's match, the latest music or fashion craze – anything to take your mind off the events of the morning. It all helps you to relax in preparation for the last burst of adrenalin; like any good athlete, you must pace yourself.

Successful Professional Reviews for Civil Engineers
ISBN 978-0-7277-6100-2

ICE Publishing: All rights reserved
http://dx.doi.org/10.1680/sprce61002.105

Chapter 16
The Written Exercise

Purpose

This final part of the Review brings the whole jigsaw to completion, locking all the pieces together. It is often said that this part is the most common cause of failure, but analysing the figures in rather more depth, it quickly becomes clear that if the written work is removed from the statistics, the Review pass rate hardly alters. This means that those whose written work is inadequate are generally also found wanting in other aspects, or pieces, of the jigsaw.

The implication is therefore that all the main pieces of the jigsaw will become connected to this final piece – all your experience and expertise from the report and supporting documents, and your CPD. We have even known instances where the Reviewers felt that a candidate did not give as good an answer as they were capable of during the interview and so asked the same question again for the Written Exercise.

In our search for guidance to help potential candidates, we eventually found what we consider to be the most useful and concise guidance in Francis Bacon's address to Gresham College, London, which we paraphrase below:

> carry on your discussions with clarity and power and rigorousness, in
> recognisable sequences of enquiry, discovery, expansion, challenges and
> conclusion, all conducted with reason and addressed to any subject that takes
> your fancy.

(Francis Bacon, 1561–1626)

Francis Bacon was one of the first Britons to relate scientific discovery to practical problems through meticulous research and progressive experiment. It is perhaps fitting that, as an early exponent of what we would now describe as engineering thought, he should also have produced a description which we believe is of inestimable use to civil engineers.

In the context of the Professional Reviews, we believe that it is reasonable to divide the types of question you could be asked into four broad categories:

(a) *Factual* e.g. 'Outline the stages in the development of a design for a (bridge/dam/ leisure centre . . .) from the initial brief to the issue of working drawings, giving examples from your own experience'.

(b) *Expository* e.g. 'List the records which should be kept by the employer's agent responsible for the construction of a wastewater treatment works. Describe the content and function of each item'.

(c) *Argumentative* e.g. 'Discuss the advantages and disadvantages of off-site modular fabrication'.

(d) *Visionary* e.g. 'Engineers are born not made. Discuss'.

In general, though not invariably, the first two types of question are usual for the Member Professional Review. You are expected to be able to communicate, in writing, facts and procedures with which you should be familiar, since the questions are based on your direct experience. This type of exercise should enable you to demonstrate:

- the ability to marshal information quickly into a reasoned order to a tight deadline
- that you are decisive, clear thinking, and can put a reasoned and logical description together quickly
- that you are able to explain something with which you are familiar to someone who is not
- that you have an incisive ability to 'see the wood from the trees', not getting immersed in repetitive or irrelevant detail.

These are the characteristics of any competent professional engineer.

The latter two styles of question ask you to state and justify your own views and opinions and are perhaps more representative of the questions set for the Chartered Professional Review. There is no 'correct' answer to such questions. Indeed, the Reviewers are expressly told that they cannot mark a candidate down merely because the views expressed differ from their own, with one very important proviso – that the views are not mere prejudice, but are ones which could reasonably be developed from the experience of the candidate. These latter question types enable you to demonstrate all the above-listed qualities, with the addition of:

- independence of thought and opinion
- a professional attitude, integrity and honesty
- judgement for the benefit of the general public good
- wide knowledge and understanding of current affairs

all attributes of a leader of the profession – a Chartered Engineer.

These scripts are not in any way like the written examinations taken during an academic course; they are *not* a test of knowledge, but a test of your ability to communicate as a professional engineer. Knowledge is used to *support* your responsible reasoning and arguments (hence the marking of 'relevance' – of your knowledge to the question and to your opinions).

Method of approach to the Written Exercise

Consider the keywords which come out of Bacon's definition, coupled with the notes in the Institution guidance, and compile them into the framework or pattern:

Enquiry	What does the set question mean?
	Why has it been asked?
	What does it imply?
	What lies behind it?
	How am I going to attempt or endeavour to answer it?
Discovery	This is the thinking part of the process, where you explore all the relevant facts and knowledge you can think of. You will be searching for references and background material. Then you must marshal your thoughts into a logical sequence.
Expansion	Where does the question lead? Can you determine the full extent of your answer and develop a line of reasoning or argument?
	Can you extrapolate from the immediate answer to the question to broaden your discussion sufficiently?
	Do you have the relevant knowledge to support your statements or opinions?
Challenge	Can you provoke thought or debate in the Reviewers' minds?
	State your own views positively and concisely.
Conclusion	Summarise your own personal thoughts or arguments.
	Do not introduce new material. The conclusion must be a logical summary of what you have already said.
	If you are running out of time, then list the outstanding matters you hoped to discuss.

In effect, your written work leads the reader from the question, through a reasoned and logical discussion or explanation which they should follow and accept, to a conclusion which sets out *your* views on, or understanding of, the answer to the question, with which (hopefully) the reader will then agree, or which will provoke them into thinking more about it themselves.

Newspaper editorials are a useful source of ideas on approach; note how, while the content differs from day to day, the format or 'technique' is nearly always the same every day. One useful technique is to compare a news item as described in a broadsheet to the same item in a tabloid. The journalists who work for the tabloids are experts at minimising the word count but still getting the story across. This is what you need to do.

Again, the phrase, 'Tell them what you are going to tell them, tell them, then tell them what you have told them' is pertinent. We do not think this is particularly relevant in this situation, where time will not allow much repetition but, nevertheless, we believe you should tell the Reviewers how you are going to answer the question (which may identify matters you will not have time to cover), answer the question and then draw the whole thing to a conclusion by summarising what you have just said.

Preparation

The purpose of the Written Exercise is to allow you to demonstrate your ability to communicate in writing through scrutiny of the following aspects:

- The way in which the content relates to the question – this includes the factual content and the way in which various aspects of the subject are analysed, compared and contrasted and conclusions reached.
- The structure – there must be a clearly identifiable *introduction* displaying the main aspects of the topic; a *development*, in which the topic is considered in detail and the main and subsidiary arguments set out; a *conclusion*, in which the threads of the discussion are drawn together and conclusions reached.
- The quality of the English – this relates not only to grammar and spelling, but also to sentence and paragraph construction and style.

Technique

The Reviewers look upon candidates as potential senior managers who will be required to present reports or advice to laymen, so a reasonably high standard is expected. Our profession's past inability to express itself clearly (except, of course, to other engineers) has contributed to a lack of public confidence. It is worthwhile therefore giving some time to perfecting a technique; there are several complementary ways in which this can be achieved:

- Attendance on a course. There are many available but look at the format in detail; you must consider carefully what you need:
  - Is a concentrated course better than, say, joining one of the Institution's Written Exercise groups?
  - Is your weakness the use of language, grammar and syntax or breadth of knowledge?
  - Would it help if your practice exercises were marked?
  There are some very good distance learning packages which enable you to work around your normal work commitments.
- A selective programme of reading – this includes publications relating not just to technical matters in which you are involved but to your profession, management generally and the political, financial and environmental framework within which we operate.

■ Development of a critical awareness in the workplace, not merely of your own involvement but of the whole environment within which you operate.

■ If you intend to hand-write your exercise then you should undertake suitable practice under 'examination conditions'; this is important. Invigilators have reported that too many candidates are *physically* unfit for the Written Exercise (i.e. they cannot write for over an hour without discomfort). After all, when was the last time you wrote *continuously* for that length of time – during your college or university days? If you are thinking about cramp and discomfort, you cannot be concentrating on what you are writing.

The Written Exercise questions (two, from which you must select one) are set from your submission; it is expected that you will know at least enough to answer either of them. (If not, the Reviewers have found you out – your report has misled them!) Do read both questions and make sure you understand what the Reviewers want; it helps if you underline the keywords. Do you understand what is required by 'Discuss', 'Describe', 'Comment', etc? But remember, unlike much of what you have written over the past several years, this is not primarily a test of knowledge; it is a test of how well you can communicate your knowledge to a layman (that is, someone of equivalent intelligence but without your specific knowledge). In this respect it differs markedly from most, if not all, of the written communication you carried out during your academic education.

Planning

Do not choose one of the questions without a few minutes' thought. It is surprising just how many scripts start on one answer and, after a few lines, the candidate has crossed it all out and started again on the other. Not only have they put themselves at a considerable time disadvantage, they have also given their confidence a nasty jolt.

Do not start the actual writing without adequate planning. Think about the answers to both questions for about five minutes, then move on to develop a plan for the one with which you feel most confident.

At the start of the assignment, 25 or 30 minutes will seem like a lifetime – all your instincts will be screaming at you to start and everyone around you will be scribbling or typing frantically. But control yourself, secure in the knowledge that previous experience under similar conditions has made you confident you can write sufficient in the remaining time.

Planning is itself assessed – any drafts, notes, plans, etc. should be submitted to the invigilator, if you are to receive any credit for your planning. Once you have decided on a plan, stick to it and finish it – your Reviewers will not be impressed if you cannot even fulfil your own plan. Monitor progress by deleting each idea once it has been incorporated.

Ideas will spring to mind in a very haphazard way when you begin to think. It is important to jot down every idea in note form as it occurs, however random and irrelevant it seems. Based on many years' experience of marking assignments from the Reviews, we know that many trainee engineers do not actually know how to plan a document. Most merely list the items they will discuss, but although a list may be the plan it certainly is not planning. There are inexpensive books available on mind maps and planning which are well worth reading if you have difficulty with this aspect.

The 'brain dumping' after the initial blank panic at the start will, generally speaking, begin with the answers to the question, followed by 'less important' material to provide enough to write 1000 words. The temptation is to follow the same logical process, answer the question in the first few pages and then proceed to justify the answer; the result is that the essay tails away.

It is better to start by filling in the background first, arriving at the answer at the end (i.e. invert the list). In this way you lead the reader to a firm conclusion. But beware! Do not pad out the start with irrelevancies; how many times have we seen a Reviewer's comment somewhere about page three, 'Answer starts here' – not a good omen!

Once all your ideas are recorded, you can assemble them in a logical order; there are several ways of doing this:

(*a*) simply numbering each idea in a sequence and then rewriting in the correct order
   – the danger here is that it is relatively easy to miss one out
(*b*) lettering (or using a colour code) to identify each idea with its appropriate
   paragraph and then numbering each within the paragraph, finally rewriting in the
   correct sequence
(*c*) spider (spoke) diagrams where ideas radiate outwards from the central question,
   each being assigned to the most appropriate 'leg' – each leg subsequently becomes
   a paragraph
(*d*) 'noughts and crosses framework', achieved by dividing the answer into three parts,
   each containing three paragraphs. Each idea as it occurs is put into the most
   appropriate 'box'. This is a highly structured technique which requires practice,
   but is very useful for writing short reports.

Do not get carried away with one particular aspect to the detriment of others; try to achieve a *balance* in both content and depth of treatment. Planning methods (*d*) and (*c*) and, to a lesser extent, (*b*) clearly highlight any such imbalance since one square or leg will become overloaded. If it does, reconsider the distribution, consider adding another paragraph or perhaps you are entering into too much detail on this aspect.

Planning gives you the structure of the body of the assignment, especially the paragraphs. A paragraph is a collection of sentences all on a particular theme. Change the theme –

start a new paragraph. The use of paragraphs demonstrates control over ideas and their expression. A good answer contains paragraphs of variable length, each containing material on one aspect only. The paragraphs themselves should follow a logical sequence, avoiding abrupt changes in direction which disconcert the reader.

Format

The Reviewers will also consider how effectively you introduce and conclude the answer. The opening sentence must attract interest and make the reader want to read on; a short, sharp first sentence is the most effective. It can be a good idea to rewrite the question and outline your approach to it – this helps to ensure that you do actually answer the set question and not the one you thought (or hoped) it was.

The Reviewers may use words which are not yet universally understood: for example, just what is 'the infrastructure' or 'pollution'? *Infra* comes from the Latin for 'under' so does it mean 'under the structure' or 'under the ground'? Or does it refer to all the systems which enable movement of goods, people, supplies, waste and energy? Or does it encompass (as most politicians seem to believe) the entire built environment? Are 'pollutants' merely in the wrong place or are they actually causing harm? If such words are used in the question then, for the avoidance of doubt, start by defining *your* understanding of the word. It doesn't matter if it is not identical to the Reviewers' interpretation, as long as it is sensible.

There must be a conclusion, a 'summing-up'; even if you are short of time, at least a 'one-liner'. Avoid dullness and assumptions; do not introduce further information; do make sure that your development does actually lead to the conclusion you have reached. The conclusion must be positive – do not let the essay just peter out.

The Reviewers are looking for understanding supported by facts. Do not be afraid to express original ideas and opinions (as long as they are sensible and you justify them) rather than regurgitating stereotyped 'popular' views. Present points in an orderly, uncomplicated way to demonstrate logical, clear and, if possible, original thought. Substantiate each point with facts or figures, wherever possible taken from your own experience. You have met your Reviewers by then – do not fall into the trap of subconsciously writing for them, knowing as you do that they already know a great deal about the subject – the result will be superficial and unacceptable.

Clarity and presentation

Make the script look organised and authoritative, whether handwritten or typed. If you opt for the former, then practise handwriting if yours is rather scruffy and difficult to read. In any case, when was the last time you wrote for an hour without a break – you need the practice! Try to keep the handwriting consistent throughout, so that once the Reviewers are used to it they can read it easily. If all of this is difficult for you, then consider the use of a laptop, but do read and digest our advice at the end of this chapter.

Indent paragraphs in a consistent way – begin on the next line (no space between paragraphs) about 3 cm from the left-hand margin.

Remember that the Reviewers are reading your work in their own time and may well be tired; make it clear, readily understandable and enjoyable, but avoid making jokes – they will inevitably be taken the wrong way and do not appear professional!

Avoid lapsing into jargon or slang; do not use words like rebar, shutters, dumper or lab. This is not easy, because we use both jargon and slang every day in discussions with other engineers, but these terms are not considered appropriate in the written word.

Under no circumstances use several words where one would do because you think the script may be a bit short; this will only draw the Reviewers' attention to the deficiency and probably annoy them. If you use abbreviations or acronyms, on the first occasion write the term out in full, followed by the acronym in brackets.

Practice

To be successful in the Written Exercise, it is vital to practise under the supervision of someone (not necessarily another engineer) who can comment, not so much on the content, but on the 'readability'. They need to be asked such questions as: 'Do you see what I am getting at?', 'Can you follow my argument?', 'Does it make sense?' and 'Did you enjoy reading it?' Such a person need not be an engineer; in fact sometimes it is a positive benefit if they are not familiar with the subject. They will ask questions which cause you to think whether or not you did actually write what you intended, or whether there is a better way of explaining that particular matter.

Having watched a large number of candidates writing and discussed the problems with them and the Reviewers, we are absolutely certain that there is no substitute for practice. Not just in writing answers, but in writing them under severe time constraints. Anyone can write an acceptable answer in a fortnight; it takes skill, time management and clear, quick thinking to do it adequately in a couple of hours. A long letter from a friend once concluded, 'I am sorry this letter turned out to be so long. I did not have the time to write a shorter one!'.

We have become concerned when we visit ICE Written Exercise groups at the amount of time and effort spent collecting knowledge – generally far too much for regurgitating in the given time, particularly given the bespoke nature of the questions posed by Reviewers. All that many of these groups are in fact doing is giving their members an additional problem – too great a choice of available information! By all means discuss and read around the subjects, but then distil this information into key points, which can be introduced into many of the questions. It is our considered view that most Written Exercise groups would be much more effective if they concentrated more on practice than on collecting information.

The other concern we have is the predilection for 'model' answers. Now that the Written Exercise is 'open book', and the questions must be specific to your particular experience, it is highly unlikely that any Reviewer will ask you a stock question. If you have never been involved in joint ventures, then you will not be asked a question about them. Even in a group from the same organisation, the answers will be different, reflecting the differing experience of the members. Model answers may give you a lead and a general shape to an answer, but you must bring your own perspective to them.

You need a working knowledge of the whole range of civil engineering, not merely a high degree of specialist technical knowledge, so that you can relate your expertise to the environment in which you work. And you need to immerse yourself in well-written, well-structured papers, magazines and books so that you subconsciously absorb their style and techniques.

English as a foreign language

The language of the Engineering Council is English, so anyone wishing to register with them as CEng, IEng or EngTech, must demonstrate that they have a reasonable facility with it. The Institution can and does offer membership outside the UK, where the Written Exercise is done in the candidate's own language, but then cannot recommend the candidate to the Engineering Council. Since the Engineering Council's jurisdiction only extends to the UK, this is usually of no relevance.

You are trying to prove you are a professional engineer and, as such, any reports or documents which go out from your organisation would be expected to be of a consistently high standard. So, as we mentioned in Chapter 10, your reports and submission must be perfect. As a responsible engineer, you are expected to have taken any necessary steps to ensure this, whether English is your first language or not.

The standard expected for the written work in the afternoon of the Review is different. The documents state 'a final draft'. In other words, not perfect, but tidy and logical, capable of being edited by someone without your technical background, and without having to refer back to you because the sense of what you are trying to say has been lost.

Again, your curiosity should have been aroused by the wording in the ICE requirements, where it says 'in acceptable English'. Acceptable is perhaps an unexpected adjective, but it allows the Reviewers the freedom to make a judgement – acceptable in the context of the background of the candidate. Someone who has come to the UK in the past few years may not be as proficient with the language as someone who was born here. Someone who routinely writes reports to government departments or authorities will be expected to have more fluent skills than someone more used to writing requisition orders and daily progress reports. The Reviewers are seeking to confirm that each candidate is capable of communicating in writing in their particular context.

This judgement applies also to dyslexia, provided you are able to inform the Institution at the time of submission by supplying a certificate defining your condition. There is sometimes dispensation on the time allowed but all written work by dyslexic candidates is automatically referred to a special panel with access to appropriate medical advice.

Reference material

The Written Exercise is 'open book', so in theory you can take anything in. But think carefully: what do you actually need. For instance, we have difficulty remembering exact quotations (such as 'sustainability') or their sources (the United Nation's Brundtland Commission of 1983) so we suggest that you should have a list of relevant quotes, their sources and dates.

Resist the temptation to take too much, because you are not sure what you may need. You cannot spare the time to search through a great stack of papers and books. The ultimate reference tool is surely the hard drive on your computer or the internet, but do read what we say about this in the next section.

Computer use

You may be surprised that we have left this to the end of the chapter. But everything we have said so far about the Written Exercise is applicable whether you use a laptop or not. We have discussed with many candidates their wish to use a computer. Some say it is because their handwriting is not legible when under pressure, and we think this is a valid reason.

We are not at all convinced by another common reason: that candidates believe they can write faster on a laptop than they can by hand. We think that, in many cases, this dependency is merely an attempt to mask an inability to marshal your thoughts and compose a logical discussion in your mind, before transmitting them.

If you believe that you are going to be able to disguise any weakness in your capacity to swiftly rally your ideas and compose them into a logical discussion by resorting to frequent use of cut-and-paste, then you may well run out of time or produce a disjointed script. The Reviewers say that they can usually quickly identify such a technique because the script just does not flow.

Finally, there is the apparent comfort of the hard drive memory (permitted) or the internet (prohibited)! Most Review venues have wi-fi available and also it is usually easy to connect your laptop to cellular data services without the need to use wi-fi. All such connections are prohibited by the Institution. If you seriously believe that you are going to have the time to use Google or search your hard drive to collect relevant facts and information about the question, and then arrange them into some sort of coherent answer, you are deluding yourself on several counts:

- Your Reviewers will ask you questions to which you ought to know the answer anyway, so you should not need the reassurance of comprehensive details stored in external memories.
- You may well fall into the trap, mentioned earlier, of actually having too much material to transmit in the time available, giving you the added difficulty of making choices under pressure.
- The Reviewers know that you intend to use a computer, and so will not ask any questions to which you may have stored a previously compiled model answer.

The ICE uses similar sophisticated detection software to many universities and you may well be caught if you copy someone else's work. In any case, most competent readers can detect plagiarism very easily, because the style changes.

If you need the support of your computer memory or the internet, are you actually attempting the Review too early? Your apparent dependence on stored material does perhaps suggest that you personally doubt whether you really do understand what you are doing or the wider implications of your work.

So do think hard about why you wish to use a laptop and ensure that your reasons are valid.

You should also ensure that you have familiarised yourself with the Institution's rules and guidance for the use of laptops at Review. We have not described those here, as they are prone to occasional change. As a minimum, ensure that your laptop is fully charged, in good working order and that its automatic backup settings are enabled, just in case of technical problems.

Successful Professional Reviews for Civil Engineers
ISBN 978-0-7277-6100-2

ICE Publishing: All rights reserved
http://dx.doi.org/10.1680/sprce61002.117

Chapter 17
The aftermath

You have completed the jigsaw to the very best of your ability and you now face a prolonged wait for the result. It is perhaps difficult for candidates to understand why it takes so long before the email arrives with your result letter attached.

When you leave the Review centre, the system really swings into action. The literary efforts, amounting to as many as 40 scripts each day for a month, are sorted, scanned (if handwritten) and uploaded to the Institution's reviews portal for subsequent access by the Reviewers who will read and mark your work. At this stage they will probably confer by phone or email, either to compromise where there are discrepancies in the marking, or to discuss the final completion of their paperwork about you, most of which they try to complete in the short time between each interview. Obviously they now have to add the result of the written work and confirm the tentative conclusion which they arrived at after your interview. Remember that they are all doing this in their own time and fitting it into an already busy schedule of work so there are bound to be some delays.

The Reviewers' forms, their verdict and a draft of the letter to be sent to you if you have not been successful, are then all uploaded to the reviews portal. As several hundred results arrive, the office prepares all the letters and takes the samples which will be put before expert panels for review as part of the quality assurance processes. At this stage, there may also be candidates with dyslexia whose written work is automatically reviewed by a panel. All these panels are specially convened and, again, are dependent on a number of volunteers fitting mutually convenient dates into their diaries.

Meanwhile, the staff archive all of the files and examine any responses to the announcement published in *New Civil Engineer* some time before, where the membership is asked whether anyone has any reason why the listed names (including yours) should not be admitted to the Institution, provided they are successful at the Review. Every draft failure letter is examined by another panel for any inconsistencies before being despatched.

We hope you can now see that everything possible is done to keep the suspense time to a minimum. Obviously, the results must all be announced at the same time, so all these voluntary panels, and the Institution staff, are working to tight deadlines. This is why you will definitely not get any reply to a query about the impending results. All such a phone call or email will do is delay the process for everybody – so do not be tempted.

The unsuccessful Review

When you receive your result, just open it. If you see the dreaded words 'I regret to inform you...' that is about all you will read for some time – all that effort and hard work was in vain. This is a devastating blow. There is little anyone can do to reduce its impact; the Reviewers are urged to tell you which Attributes you demonstrated and go on to tell you why they reached their decision, but the initial shock will prevent you looking at this rationally.

You will then go on to read the reasons and will become increasingly disillusioned. It is highly likely that you will disagree with what you think the letter says and feel that it is unfair. The temptation will be to march down the corridor and berate your SCE or line manager about the inadequacies of the Institution or pick up the phone and talk belligerently to your Regional support staff. Worse, you may even be tempted to write a strong letter to the President! The one thing you definitely should never do is phone the Reviewers: this is considered totally unprofessional and completely out of order. Every failure letter is put before a Standards Panel, which checks that it makes clear:

- why you were unsuccessful and
- where you satisfied the Reviewers.

We hear many candidates complaining about the content of their failure letters; just remember, before getting agitated, that they have been checked by at least four different people.

Recovering the situation

We strongly counsel caution. Wait! Wait until your initial surge of disappointment, even anger, has dissipated. You will then feel utterly dejected. It is at this stage that you need wise counsel, something which the ICE Regional staff are in a very good position to provide. They see many letters (you have seen only this one and your colleagues hopefully very few more) and they also know many of the Reviewers and their styles of writing. Additionally, they have access to advice and guidance from their colleagues on matters of detail with which they might not be familiar. So they will be able to give you an insight into what has actually been said – 'reading between the lines'.

The phrase which appears most frequently is 'You failed to demonstrate ...'. Your reaction may well be 'But it's obvious!'. Is it? Or are you expecting them to infer something which the regulations state has to be demonstrated and which has not actually been spelt out in your reports? You and your sponsors know what you were trying to write; the Reviewers can only see what you actually wrote down. Did you actually say what you meant?

You may feel that you were not given adequate opportunities during the interview to display your expertise; you must ask the question 'Why?'. Had the Reviewers come to the conclusion that it was not worth pursuing this matter? Your interview should not have been a cross-examination – poking relentlessly at a weakness may only cause a candidate to become defensive and is unlikely to allow them to present themselves favourably, so most Reviewers change the subject. Could you, in fact, have demonstrated it or have they actually identified a real weakness?

The letter usually concludes by suggesting that, before you submit again, you should seek advice from senior engineers, including your Regional support staff, which you should certainly do.

Rectifying any problems

There will be one of two outcomes from the analysis of the detail of the letter – either you did 'fail to demonstrate' or the Reviewers actually did identify a weakness. The former can fairly readily be rectified in the next submission, while the latter will take some time. In extreme cases, it may be that they have exposed fundamental weaknesses, either personal or in your experience, which make another attempt unwise. They may suggest that it may be more suitable for you to divert to a different, more appropriate Review, certainly for the time being. This is a formidable personal decision to have to make and we urge anyone in this difficult situation to discuss it with as many informed people as they feel able. Do not keep mulling it over yourself – you will not resolve the problem, it will merely loom larger.

Any small shortfall must be put right by further experience; it may be that the Reviewers have given an indication of how this could be achieved. But they will never tell you what you need to do, which can be frustrating. But how can they, when they have no idea of your circumstances, either personal or in the workplace? You need to talk it through with key personnel in your organisation, perhaps engineers who sponsored you, to identify opportunities for suitable experience which might become available, or could be made available, to rectify this weakness and how you could take best advantage of them. Perhaps the problem was with the written work, in which case it may be advisable to enrol on an appropriate course. This could be one of the many specifically aimed at the Reviews, or it could be a more fundamental course on the use of the English language.

The revised submission

You need to review your entire submission to see whether the various documents can be adjusted to cover the weaknesses perceived last time. You will have had, in the interim, further experience, which might be more appropriate for the Professional Review Report.

Every Review is a complete entity.

119

Do not make the fundamental mistake of believing that you have passed most of the Review and now only need to rectify the few shortcomings, either perceived or real. You are taking the whole Review again (remember the holistic review described in Chapter 4) – with one important difference. This time the Reviewers will have an additional document – a copy of your failure letter from the Institution. This puts you at a slight disadvantage, so you must get back to the status quo as quickly as possible.

To do this, we believe you must answer the letter which has been copied to the Reviewers. We think it entirely appropriate that you write to each of them (as part of your revised submission), explaining precisely what you have done, in the way of additional experience, Continuing Professional Development and training or in rewriting the submission and amending the supporting documents, to rectify the faults (perceived or otherwise) found last time. This is a totally professional approach; otherwise they will not know what you have done to rectify problems and you will have to try to explain during your interview, which just shortens the time available for them to find out whether you now comply with the requirements and really are a professional engineer.

Successful Professional Reviews for Civil Engineers
ISBN 978-0-7277-6100-2

ICE Publishing: All rights reserved
http://dx.doi.org/10.1680/sprce61002.121

Chapter 18
Technical Report route (TRR)

This route is almost worth a book on its own. In an ideal world, perhaps a separate volume would be a better solution, because it is significantly different from all the other ICE Reviews. Keeping it separate would accentuate the differences. This is why we have left this chapter to the end.

Like the other chapters, however, this one again concentrates on the philosophy and purposes; you are expected to pick up the rules and regulations from the Institution's publications, which can be downloaded from the ICE website.

When revising many of its other routes to membership in early 2015, the Institution did not amend the TRR. It may, however, do so and you should check the most recent requirements and advice on the ICE website. The advice contained here reflects the requirements current in March 2015.

Eligibility

The TRR to membership is for those engineers who have progressed to roles normally filled by either Chartered or Incorporated members, but who lack the necessary academic qualifications and are unable to top them up.

There is a mistaken belief that it is the route for all those whose age exceeds the minimum; this is not the case and, in fact, would subject many, who have already satisfied the academic base, to a more onerous route than is necessary through the more conventional reviews.

Equally erroneous is the minority belief that anyone with the requisite number of years of experience is automatically eligible to pursue this route. Look again at the rules, which imply that you must have been in positions of increasing responsibility. It is clear that, unless you have made considerable career progression so that you are virtually operating in the role of a professional engineer, then you are probably not eligible. This is not a back-door route; it is onerous and rigorous.

So, the very first thing to do is to decide which is the most appropriate grade of membership for you. Compare your current role with the criteria referred to in Chapter 6 and make an honest judgement about yourself. One of the reasons why there is a preliminary submission for this route is that far too many people seem to believe that merely because they have a lot of experience in civil engineering and have reached maturity, they have a chance of success. This is just not true!

Far better to persuade yourself at the outset of the most suitable and realistic goal, than to aim too high and be told, after a large amount of effort and a considerable period of time and several interviews, that your experience has not developed the required levels of ability. There is little room for potential, as there might be for a younger engineer; at the time you submit you must have, to all intents and purposes, become a professional engineer.

The second thing to do before you start in earnest is to make quite certain that your academic qualifications are not acceptable and that you therefore cannot utilise the conventional, and rather less onerous, routes. To some extent, this depends not only on what your qualifications are, but also on exactly when, and perhaps where, you achieved them. The rules are complex and you need to get informed advice and guidance from the Institution. Many qualifications gained outside the UK are (or can be) ratified, so even if your degree or diploma is not apparently eligible, do check. You could save yourself a significant amount of effort.

So, for this Review, you have two things to prove: first, that you are operating at a level of responsibility commensurate with that of the professional qualification you seek and, second, that you have achieved a standard of technical and academic competence comparable with that possessed by an academically qualified engineer in the same position of responsibility.

It is this second requirement which seems to cause the greatest difficulty in the progression – mainly, we think, because candidates concentrate exclusively on proving their professional capability. This is, after all, probably the thing which makes them want to become professionally qualified in the first place.

By and large, your Experience Report provides the means to prove that you are operating at a sufficiently high level of responsibility, while your Technical Report will demonstrate your understanding of technical principles. It is vital that you keep this distinction in mind throughout your preparation of the documents.

If you have both the competencies set out in the appropriate Appendix A of the *Professional Review Guidance* and these *indicative* years of increasingly responsible experience listed by the Institution, then TRR is an option:

	IEng	CEng
Accredited BEng/BSc or equivalent	–	7 years
Accredited Higher National Diploma/Certificate or equivalent	5 years	10 years
Approved National Diploma/National Certificate	10 years	–
No appropriate qualifications	15 years	15 years

Note: The qualifications listed above are specific to the UK, though other countries' academic awards will be assessed in a similar way.

Before starting on this route, engineers are required to submit a CV, a synopsis of their proposed Technical Report and the name of a mentor. This is so that the Institution can determine whether there is a reasonable chance of success, thus avoiding abortive work and unrealistic expectations.

Do not produce the synopsis before you at least have a draft report. We have encountered many candidates who have written and submitted a draft and then found they could not write the Technical Report to back it up! This synopsis is critical and is frequently a stumbling block for a large proportion of candidates. So, again, it needs careful construction, targeting the criteria laid down. The ICE gives very clear guidance on the areas of your knowledge you need to demonstrate. You should make sure that both your synopsis and the eventual Technical Report show how you match the criteria.

Submission

The submission consists of a Technical Report, an Experience Report and a record of CPD. Remember that the overriding requirement for CPD is an average of thirty hours (five days) per working year, so do not believe that the specification for the conventional route necessarily applies to you. If you have many years' experience, it is likely that you no longer have a record of CPD from years ago; but at least show what you have done over the last few years, say six or seven as a minimum.

Technical Report

The requirement is for a report between 3000 and 10 000 words in length. In our experience as Reviewers, the most effective length seems to be around 5000 words. It must be an exposition of your major role in some aspect of civil engineering, showing how you resolved technical problems by the application of engineering principles and knowledge. It must show how your experience has compensated for your lack of formal education in your particular chosen technical discipline. Do not fall into the trap (as many do) of inadvertently straying into demonstrating your overall professional capability; you are demonstrating that you have a similar understanding of the technical principles underlying your work as is required by the standard educational base.

To do this successfully, almost invariably, requires you to do some swotting. Few engineers at this relatively advanced stage in their careers, are deeply involved in the day-to-day resolution of technical problems. Rather, you find such problems and then delegate their detailed resolution to skilled technical colleagues.

Guiding several TRR applicants, Mac has found that it can be helpful to write this report as a hypothetical talk for final-year undergraduates, explaining how the theory that the students are learning has enabled the candidate to solve a significant engineering problem. This means that it is probably useful to have access (through a colleague or a university lecturer) to degree course notes for the subject you have chosen.

If you do not do the detailed calculations yourself, then it is very likely that you do discuss the problem, help identify possible solutions and have an input into the choice of the most appropriate one. To do this with credibility, you have to gain the trust of the colleagues who carry out the detailed analysis; they have to believe that you understand their diffi-culties and will not ask for anything stupid or unrealistic. So you *do* probably understand the technical principles to some extent. Now you really have to get to know the analytical details. You are not expected to be able to do the calculations, but you should develop sufficient understanding of the principles to be able to look at the solution and decide for yourself whether it 'looks right'. Your expert colleagues are the people to help you with this, so gain their co-operation.

You will also probably need to study relevant textbooks and, again, your colleagues will be able to refer you to the most suitable. Nearly all successful candidates have found it necessary to read in depth and study around their subject area in order to be able to demonstrate an adequate understanding. It is rather like students taking their final academic examinations – during which they are required to memorise and quote various formulae and equations which, under normal work situations, they would look up in an appropriate textbook. You will be expected to be able to do something similar during your Review. This process may seem a trifle artificial and unrealistic, but does it differ much from the academic situation you are being asked to replicate, where the average undergraduate swots for their final examinations?

The great danger when writing this report is that you inadvertently set out to prove you are good at your job. A number of candidates have fallen into this trap and have been unsuccessful as a result. The Reviewers are probably reasonably convinced already of your overall capability from your responsibilities at work. What they need you to demonstrate in this report is that you fully understand the engineering principles behind the solutions to some of your technical problems. You must ensure that your Technical Report demonstrates how you meet the criteria set out in the ICE guidance for the route.

Experience Report

This report requires you to deliver exactly the same messages as a conventional candidate: 2000 words emphasising your burgeoning experience and contribution, clearly showing how you developed the attributes of a professional engineer. The latter part of this report will demonstrate how you used these attributes to drive projects to a successful conclusion. So it is similar to the Professional Review Report required of conventional candidates, for which guidance is given in Chapters 10 and 11.

To be successful, you must use the greater part of the report to outline your current role and responsibilities, with just a brief sketch of the career which enabled you to reach that level of competence. It therefore seems sensible to write it in reverse chronological order, first describing what you are currently doing in a little over half the word allowance, and then use the rest to outline how you got there.

Summary of preparation

Throughout the preparation of these two components, you must keep in mind the requirements for a conventional candidate. In general, your Experience Report will tell the Institution what experience you have been exposed to; more importantly, it will tell them all the benefits you gained from that experience and how you now use the competencies you have developed. It is vital that you write this document with these targets in mind, otherwise you will join the long list of people who have told the Institution only what they have done, and failed to tell them of the benefits they gained.

The Technical Report, on the other hand, is likely to be a more theoretical document, covering matters beyond your immediate day-to-day involvement. It is vital that you keep this distinction clear in your mind.

Much later on in the process, when your application is referred to the Engineering Council, you will be asked to write for them a brief explanation of why you believe you should be allowed to be a professional engineer. Surely it makes sense to take their description of an engineer (at the appropriate grade) and use this to describe yourself through your work? There are not many differences between their criteria and those of ICE, but it is worth discovering what they are. In this way you should cover all the aspects which the Engineering Council will be seeking. It is worth thinking about this, and perhaps producing a draft, at an early stage because, again, it will focus your mind on exactly what you are trying to prove.

Choosing your Lead Sponsor

You are asking this person to fulfil an onerous task, which will involve them in deciding for themselves whether you stand a reasonable chance of success and then reading and advising during the preparation of your documents and attending meetings with you. To fulfil these duties, they must not only have an up-to-date knowledge of the requirements of the appropriate grade of membership, but must also understand and appreciate the essential differences between the reports you are about to prepare and those prepared by conventional candidates. This latter aspect is vital; we have counselled several unsuccessful candidates who have received advice, given in the utmost good faith by established Reviewers of conventional candidates or current SCEs, but which has been incorrect for this route.

If it is at all possible, the best sponsor is one who both knows the Institution's Review criteria and is also an expert in the technical field you have chosen. The Institution can often help in identifying suitable persons, but it is up to you to approach them and gain their co-operation. For the Technical Report in particular, seriously consider whether you can find an academic lecturer in your chosen subject area: they know what technical principles they teach to undergraduates and so approach your report with the correct perspective.

We strongly suggest that at an early stage, after you have selected a Lead Sponsor, you both arrange a meeting with the Institution's Regional Team for your area, so that you can be sure that your proposed plan of action fully conforms with the system and that all parties are absolutely clear on what is to be demonstrated.

Review

There are three distinct parts to the TRR review:

- Academic Review
- Professional Review
- Written Exercise.

Academic Review

During this first review, your Reviewers will make sure that you have proved to them that you meet the criteria set out for the Technical Report and thus possess the required level of academic knowledge for the class of membership for which you are applying.

This review commences with a presentation by you, taking up to 30 minutes. This is the opportunity to extend the information you have already provided in your Technical Report. Do not simply repeat it. Half an hour is a relatively long time, and you must plan the content carefully to ensure you display an in-depth understanding of the principles behind the report.

The presentation is followed by about an hour of questions, testing the range and depth of knowledge of the subject you chose for the Technical Report. One of your Reviewers may well be an academic, and they will expect you to demonstrate the same understanding and knowledge of the technical principles as a conventional university graduate. They will not range over the full prospectus of a university, but concentrate solely on the subject you have chosen.

There is then a short break, during which the two Reviewers will agree on whether or not you have convinced them. If not, the Review will be terminated. If you have, then you will be recalled for the second interview.

Professional Review

Conditional upon success in the first part, the criteria for this interview are the same as for the conventional Professional Review. You may make another presentation, which will be very different from the one you gave earlier. This time you are reinforcing and expanding your case to become a professionally qualified engineer. You will then be questioned, exactly like a conventional candidate, until the Reviewers are convinced that you have all the attributes they are seeking so that they may confirm that you are a professional engineer.

Written Exercise

You may be set a Written Exercise, at the Reviewers' discretion within ICE guidelines, dependent upon your experience. If you have more than fifteen years' experience then you will not have to complete the written assignment. If, for example, it is clear from your role at work that you are capable of writing good reports under pressure and have submitted exemplary documentation, then the Reviewers may conclude that there is little reason to test this ability at Review.

If you are required to do a Written Exercise, the specification is the same as for conventional candidates, except that it will be carried out after your Review and may be at a mutually convenient place remote from the Review centre. Guidance for preparation for the Written Exercise is given in Chapter 16.

Summary

The burden of proof for the TRR is stringent. British professional engineering qualifications are frequently perceived within the European context as lacking in formal academic education, so there is constant pressure on the Engineering Council to prove otherwise. Those without adequate academic qualifications can therefore expect to be examined in some considerable depth.

If the process is tackled logically and steadily, with advice and guidance at every stage, and with the will to spend time to understand the technical principles thoroughly, then there is a very good chance of success for those who are professional civil engineers in all but qualification.

The steady publication of the names of successful candidates for formal election is strong evidence that the TRR does provide a real way forward for those who might otherwise not have been able to gain the same level of professional qualification.

Successful Professional Reviews for Civil Engineers
ISBN 978-0-7277-6100-2

ICE Publishing: All rights reserved
http://dx.doi.org/10.1680/sprce61002.129

References

Buzan T (2006) *Mind Mapping*. BBC Active, London.

Engineering Council (2013) UK-Spec: UK Standard for Professional Engineering Competence (3rd ed). See http://www.engc.org.uk/professional-qualifications/standards/uk-spec (accessed 08/05/2015).

Walker T (2005) Difficult decisions – HSE's approach, Speech, HSC/E Seminar on Risk and Compensation – Striking a Balance, 22/03/2005. See http://www.hse.gov.uk/risk/timothywalker.pdf (accessed 25/11/2010).

World Commission on Environment and Development/Brundtland Commission (1987) *Our Common Future*. Oxford University Press, Oxford.

World Commission on Environment and Development (1987) Report of the World Commission on Environment and Development. United Nations General Assembly 96th Plenary Meeting, 11/12/1987.

World Health Organization (1993) Draft definition of 'health'. Sofia, Bulgaria. See www.health.gov/environment/definitionsofEnvironmentalHealth (accessed 25/11/2010).

References

Baxter T (2004) *Mind Mapping*. BBC Active, London.

Engineering Council (2013) *UK-SPEC, UK Standard for Professional Engineering Competence* (3rd edn). See http://www.engc.org.uk/professional-qualifications (accessed 08.10.2013).

Spicer T (2005) Difficult decisions – HSE's approach. Speech, HSOPE Seminar on Risk and Conservatism, Striking a Balance, 22.03.2005. See http://www.hse.gov.uk/risk/theory/spicer.pdf (accessed 25.01.2010).

World Commission on Environment and Development (Brundtland Commission) (1987) *Our Common Future*. Oxford University Press, Oxford.

World Commission on Environment and Development (1987) *Report of the World Commission on Environment and Development*. United Nations General Assembly 96th Plenary Meeting, 11.12.1987.

World Health Organization (1948) *Constitution of health*. Some guidelines. See www.health.gov.uk/.../definition-health.pdf (accessed 25.01.2010).

Successful Professional Reviews for Civil Engineers
ISBN 978-0-7277-6100-2

ICE Publishing: All rights reserved
http://dx.doi.org/10.1680/sprce61002.131

Index